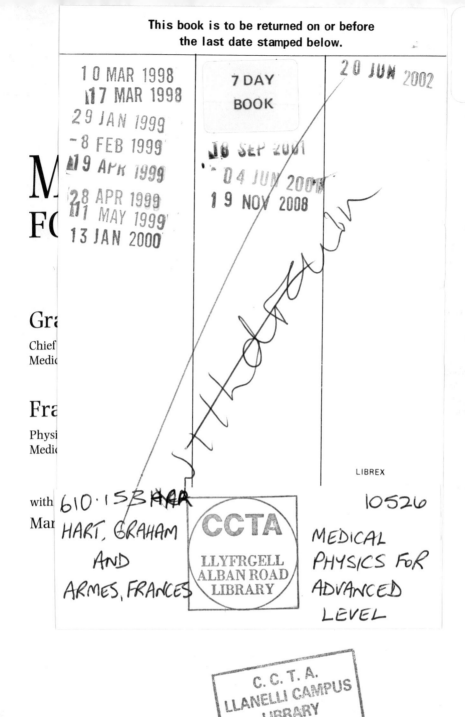

M

FO

Gra

Chief
Medic

Fra

Physi
Medic

with
Mar

Text © Graham Hart and Frances Armes 1992
Design and artwork © Simon and Schuster Education

First published 1992

Published by Simon and Schuster Education
Campus 400
Maylands Avenue
Hemel Hempstead
Herts HP2 7EZ

A catalogue record for this book is available from the British
Library.

ISBN 0 7501 0229 2

Printed and bound in Great Britain by
Dotesios Ltd, Trowbridge, Wiltshire.

Contents

Foreword

The primary aim of this book is to act as a source book to cover the requirements of the Medical Physics options in the current GCE A-level syllabuses.

The scope and depth of the book are, however, greater in many places than would be strictly necessary had it been written solely for this purpose. This has enabled coverage of almost all major areas of Medical Physics and its practice by ourselves and our colleagues in the world of medicine.

Acknowledgements

No text of this type can be produced without the help and support of a number of people. This book is no exception, and various levels of thanks must go to:

Joan Haspel at Bradford Girls Grammar School for the initial germ of the idea, for a large amount of initial background material, and for her helpful comments after the first tentative draft;

Alison Mackie, Steve Milner and Elizabeth Jefferson at Bradford Royal Infirmary, for their comments on various chapters;

David Sumner for his encouragement and his excellent book on Radiation Risks;

Philip Robinson and Janice Ward at St James' Hospital Leeds, for the magnetic resonance image;

Bryan Stubbs at Cookridge Hospital Leeds, for his help with the radiotherapy treatment plan;

Simon Hart for the cover photograph;

The National Radiological Protection Board, NE Technology Ltd, Siemens Ltd, Keeler Ltd and CIS (UK) Ltd, for permission to use certain photographs in the book;

The Joint Matriculation Board and the University of London Schools Examination Board, for permission to reproduce questions.

1

BODY MECHANICS

Bones and joints

The bones of the skeleton, numbering around 200, provide a light, strong and living framework to support the human body.

The vertebral column

Of paramount importance in this framework is the vertebral column or spine, shown in Figure 1.1, which provides the major support for the rest of the body.

The top 24 bones of the spine are classed into three groups: the seven cervical (neck) vertebrae, twelve thoracic (chest) vertebrae, and five lumbar (abdominal) vertebrae. These bones are separate, covered with fibrous **cartilage** (see below) and interspersed with resilient fibrous pads known as **discs**. It is the discs which allow the bending and twisting movements of the spine. They also protect the faces of the vertebrae during these movements from forces which would otherwise wear the bony surfaces away.

The base of the spine consists of nine fused bones known as the sacrum and coccyx. The disc separating the last lumbar vertebra and the sacrum, known as the lumbosacral disc, must carry of the order of 60% of the total body weight. It lies at an angle of approximately 40° to the horizontal, and is thus subject to both **compressive** (squashing) and **shear** (twisting) forces, particularly during bending and lifting.

Joints

The individual bones of the skeleton are held together at joints by fibrous **ligaments**. Many joints allow considerable flexibility of movement, and a range

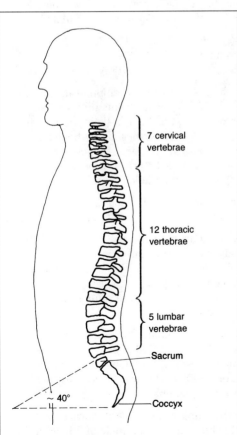

Figure 1.1   The vertebral column

7 cervical vertebrae

12 thoracic vertebrae

5 lumbar vertebrae

Sacrum

~ 40°

Coccyx

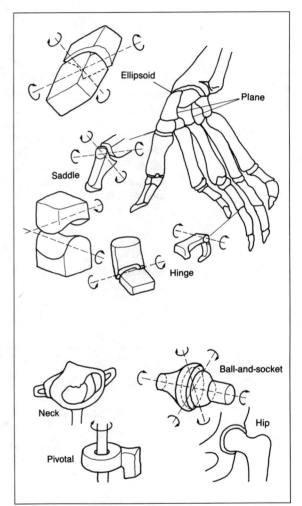

Ellipsoid

Plane

Saddle

Hinge

Neck

Ball-and-socket

Pivotal

Hip

Figure 1.2   The types of joints

of joint types exist with different kinds of flexibility, as Figure 1.2 shows.

Plane joints, such as those in the knuckles of the hand, only allow gliding movements, whereas the hinge-type joints further along the fingers permit a greater flexibility of movement. Saddle joints, such as those found in the thumb and ankle, allow a still wider range of movement.

Other types of joints allow for more specialist movements. There are pivotal joints, such as in the neck and forearm, which permit rotation; ellipsoidal joints, such as the wrist; and ball-and-socket type joints as in the shoulder and hip (see Figure 1.3), which allow the greatest range of movement.

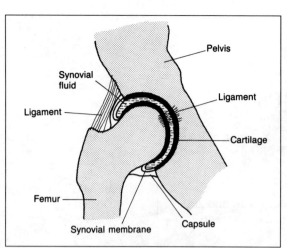

Figure 1.3 The ball-and-socket hip joint

All these joints have certain common features. They are enclosed in **capsules** of tough fibrous tissue. The ends of the bones forming the moving parts are covered by **cartilage** (gristle), a resilient, elastic material designed to protect the bones themselves. Between the layers of cartilage is **synovial fluid**, secreted to lubricate the joints.

Muscles

The bones of the skeleton move under the action of **muscles** which are attached to the skeleton by **tendons**. Muscles themselves are flexible fibrous tissue, and under the action of nerve impulses from the brain (see Chapter 4), a muscle can contract,

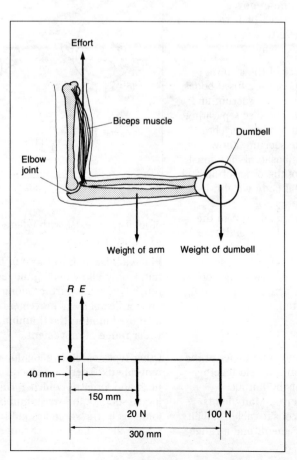

Figure 1.4 The lever action of the hand and forearm

pulling the bone with it. The muscle relaxes to restore the bone to its original position. In fact, there are usually muscles on either side of a joint, acting in opposition to one another, so that as one muscle contracts, the opposing muscle relaxes, and vice versa.

Forces and levers

A muscle, when contracting, exerts a force on the bone at the point where it is attached, producing a turning moment at the joint. The system acts as a lever, with the joint as the fulcrum. In many cases the muscle acts at a point very close to the joint, though loads at more distant points can be moved by it. The hand and forearm is a typical and convenient example, as shown in Figure 1.4.

In this example the muscle provides the effort required to move the load, which may just be the weight of the arm, but may include an additional external load, such as a dumbell held in the hand.

Taking moments about the joint allows the calculation of the effort E required to move a particular load. For this example:

$$
\begin{aligned}
E \times 0.04 &= 20 \times 0.15 + 100 \times 0.3 \\
&= 33 \\
\text{Therefore: } E &= 33 / 0.04 \\
&= 825 \text{ N}
\end{aligned}
$$

Resolving the vertical forces also allows the reaction R in the upper arm to be calculated.

$$
\begin{aligned}
\text{So: } \quad 825 &= R + 100 + 20 \\
\text{Rearranging: } R &= 825 - 100 - 20 \\
&= 705 \text{ N}
\end{aligned}
$$

It should be noted that the position of the muscle attachment near the joint means that a greater force is required to lift the arm (load) than if the muscle were attached further along the arm. However, the attachment near the joint means that a large movement of the arm can be achieved with a small change in muscle length.

Similar calculations can be made for the forces involved during bending and lifting, see Figure 1.5.

When bending at the waist, the weight W_e of the upper body (head, arms and trunk), whose combined centre of mass acts at approximately $\frac{2}{3}$ of the distance up the spine, must be supported by the muscles connecting the spine to the pelvis and the lumbosacral disc.

Under these circumstances the disc must withstand not 60% of the typical 700 N body mass (= 420 N), as it usually does in the standing position, but upwards of 2000 N. This can be demonstrated by the following equations.

Suppose the trunk leans forwards such that the vertebral column makes an angle of 70° with the vertical. The extensor muscle, which joins the spine to the pelvis, will make an angle of approximately

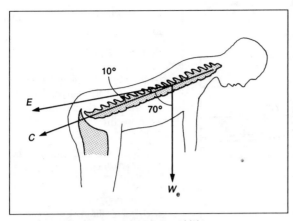

Figure 1.5   Forces during bending and lifting

$10°$ to the spine. E is the effort provided by the extensor muscle.

If the forces are resolved in the direction perpendicular to the vertebral column, then:

$$\begin{aligned} E \sin 10° &= W_e \sin 70° \\ E \times 0.17 &= 420 \times 0.94 \\ E &= 2322 \text{ N} \end{aligned}$$

The compressive force on the disc C can be calculated by resolving the forces parallel to the vertebral column.

$$\begin{aligned} \text{Here:} \quad C &= E \cos 10° + W_e \cos 70° \\ &= 2322 \times 0.98 + 420 \times 0.34 \\ &= 2418 \text{ N} \end{aligned}$$

Lifting weights of the order of 300 N in this position increases the forces on the disc to nearly 5000 N, as may be demonstrated using similar calculations. These shear and compressive forces may cause the disc to slip out of place, or rupture completely.

For this reason, lifting techniques are extremely important. If the lifting is done with the spine almost vertical, rather than in the bent position, forces on the disc can be dramatically reduced, along with the chances of damaging it.

Walking and running

While standing on the ground, the body is supported by a force which is equal and opposite to the body's own weight, and which acts vertically upwards.

As soon as the body moves relative to the ground, the magnitude and direction of that force will change. As the foot pushes off the ground, an additional force will be required to provide the necessary acceleration. Conversely, as the foot lands on the ground, a decelerating force is required to bring it to rest. Running and jumping, as might be expected, require greater forces to achieve their objectives.

The actions of movement also mean that there are horizontal components to the forces, instead of the purely vertical forces of standing. These horizontal

forces must be balanced by frictional forces between the foot and the surface. This becomes difficult when walking on slippery surfaces!

The energy balance

Input

To maintain the body's structures and functions, the cells of the body require regular inputs of energy. This energy is supplied in the form of food.

The body's digestive system breaks down the usually complex chemicals present in food into three main simpler types: carbohydrates to sugars; fats to glycerol and fatty acids; and proteins to amino acids.

The oxygen inhaled during respiration is then used to release the energy contained within the food in a variety of oxidation reactions. The chemical reactions follow the general pattern:

$$\text{fuel} + \text{oxygen} \rightarrow \text{carbon dioxide} + \text{water} + \text{energy}$$

The main source of fuel for the body comes from the sugars, principally glucose, circulating in the bloodstream. For a single molecule of glucose, the pattern above becomes:

$$C_6H_{12}O_6 + 6O_2 \rightarrow 6CO_2 + 6H_2O + 4 \times 10^{-18} \text{ J}$$

This small release of energy per molecule leads to ~ 16 kJ g^{-1} of fully oxidised glucose. Of this total energy release, $\sim 65\%$ can be converted to useful chemical processes, with the remaining 35% appearing as heat energy which maintains body temperature.

However, other reactions are possible. Glucose may, for example, be broken down to lactic acid, although this reaction is much less energy efficient, producing only 0.8 kJ g^{-1}. This type of reaction is known as **anaerobic** – it does not require oxygen. It tends to occur when the body is in extreme need of energy, such as during marathon running. As the poisonous lactic acid builds up in the muscles, the performance of the muscles is reduced. Recovery occurs when the exercise ends and sufficient oxygenated blood can re-oxidise the lactic acid. This is why massaging tired muscles, thus increasing the blood flow through them, is effective in reducing muscle fatigue.

Output

As stated previously, the body requires chemical energy to maintain its life processes or **metabolism**.

The amount of energy required to make the body 'tick over' is known as the **basal metabolic rate**, or **BMR**. The BMR varies from person to person, but there are also more significant and systematic differences, as Figure 1.6 shows.

Males have a higher average BMR than females.

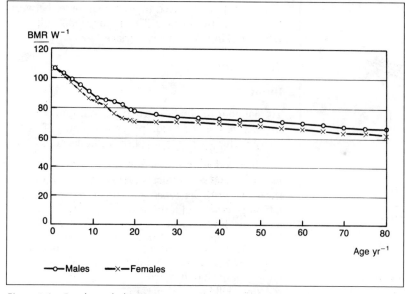

Figure 1.6   Basal metabolic rates

This occurs primarily because the lower average levels of body fat in the male mean that a greater energy output is required to maintain the body temperature.

The most significant changes to BMRs occur with age. Children have the highest BMRs, because of growth processes. After maturity, BMRs tend to level off considerably, falling slowly in old age as all bodily processes slow down.

Although the values of BMR in Figure 1.6 are averages, there are nevertheless large variations within any individual at different times. These occur due to a number of factors, such as: (a) external and internal temperatures, linked to the amount and type of clothing worn; (b) body surface area and volume; and (c) the level of exercise.

(a) Temperature

The human body functions at an internal temperature of ~37 °C, and must be kept very close to this temperature to function. Thus in cooler climates the body needs to expend more energy to keep at this temperature. In hot climates, or following strenuous exercise, the body must lose excess heat by expending energy to cool down, such as in perspiration.

(b) Body surface area and volume

The amount of energy released for body processes depends largely on tissue volume, although the rate of loss of this energy from the body is more dependent on the body's surface area. In smaller bodies (such as babies), the ratio of surface area to volume is greater, and so the potential for losses is also greater. Care must therefore be taken over the regulation of the external temperature for babies, and losses through conduction or radiation prevented by the use of appropriate clothing. Children and smaller people generally have higher

BMRs, which partially compensates for their extra losses.

(c) Exercise

Exercise is one of the greatest influences on the body's energy usage. The amount of energy expenditure rises dramatically as the level of exercise increases, as shown in Table 1.1.

Table 1.1

Type of activity	Energy usage (W)
resting	80
office work	< 170
electrical / painting / domestic work	170–350
digging / cycling / playing tennis	350–500
coal mining / playing football	500–650
furnace work / cross-country running	650–800

When summed over a full day, the energy demands of an adult will usually lie in the range 10 000–16 000 kJ, depending on the person's lifestyle.

Maintaining the balance

Under normal circumstances, energy production by the oxidation of glucose and other molecules from food is a relatively slow process, and the energy thus produced cannot be used directly in cell reactions. In reality a mediating substance known as **ATP** is involved. Energy is used to add an additional phosphate group to the molecule **adenosine diphosphate** (**ADP**), to produce the energy-rich compound **adenosine triphosphate**, or **ATP**. The energy from one molecule of glucose is sufficient to build 38 molecules of ATP. Because energy release from ATP is a direct process, the energy in ATP can be used by the body as required. ATP therefore acts as a kind of energy store, and a reserve can be built up from ADP molecules.

If more food is consumed than is required, this can also be stored in the body. For example, carbohydrates can be converted to fat, which is the major energy store of the body. When the body needs more energy than that obtainable from digested food, these fat reserves can be used to provide the extra energy.

A continuing excess of food intake will result in subsequent excess fat storage, or obesity, and may lead to a range of long-term detrimental health effects. These include heart and circulation problems such as **arteriosclerosis** – the gradual narrowing of the arteries due to the laying down of deposits within them. The extra work needed to be done by the heart and circulation to carry this excess weight should also not be discounted.

Maintaining this balance between food consumed and energy required, particularly in the affluent West, has become a difficult problem for many people!

2　VISION

Functions of the eye

Sight, like all other functions of the human body, is an extremely complex process. Rays of light from different points on an object pass through structures at the front of the eye and stimulate receptors at corresponding points on the retina. This is analogous to a camera, where light passes through the lens to form a focused image on the film. Unlike the camera, the image (which is produced by changes in intensity and wavelength) is then immediately processed by the retinal receptors to convert it into electrical signals. These pass via the optic nerve to the visual cortex in the brain for interpretation.

This procedure is more easily understood as the combination of several individual processes, i.e. image formation, image focusing, control of light intensity, sensitivity, spectral response and the persistence of vision. Before this, however, we need to examine the various structures of the eye which play an important part in these processes.

Structure of the eye

The eyes consist of two globes (eyeballs), which are set about 70 mm apart in concave recesses in the skull (the orbits). Their movements are controlled by three pairs of muscles attached to the outer

Table 2.1

Structure	Description	Purpose
sclera	thick white opaque tissue (white of eye)	protects inner structures and maintains shape of eyeball
cornea	transparent bulge at the front of the eye, refractive index 1.38	provides main refractive power of the eye
choroid	black/brown pigmented layer rich with blood vessels	reduces light reflection within the eye and supplies other structures with oxygen and nutrients
iris	pigmented diaphragm	control the amount of light entering the inner regions of the eye
pupil	central 'hole' in iris	
ciliary body	circular muscle fibres	responsible for altering the thickness of the lens
suspensory ligaments	~70 fibres attaching ciliary body to rim of lens	
lens	biconvex transparent elastic structure made up of several layers with refractive indices differing between 1.37 and 1.42	focuses the light on the retina by altering its shape
retina	light-sensitive inner layer of the eye	converts light image into electrical impulses
optic nerve	bundle of nerve fibres linking the eye to the brain	carries eletrical impulses from retina to brain
blind spot	place at which the optic nerve leaves the eye	has no light receptors, hence cannot detect images
fovea	yellowish depression just above the blind spot	provides clearest detail when image falls on it
aqueous humour	watery fluid filling front eye chamber, of refractive index 1.33	help maintain shape and firmness of eyeball
vitreous humour	jelly-like fluid filling rear eye chamber, of refractive index 1.34	

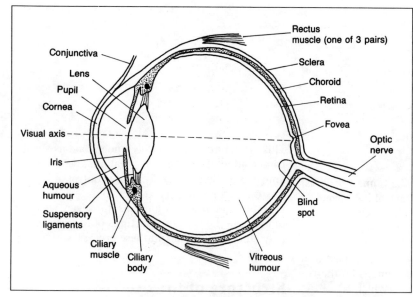

Figure 2.1   Vertical section of the eye

The retina consists of ~10^8 light-sensitive cells or receptors, called **rods** and **cones**, according to their shape. Figure 2.2 shows the sensory cells of the retina.

The distribution of these receptors is not uniform. For example, the fovea contains just cones, but the proportion of rods to cones increases with the distance from the fovea, and around the edge the retina consists mainly of rods.

Rods and cones are connected to two layers of nerve cells that pass over the surface of the retina before becoming the optic nerve at the optic disc. Light must pass through this nerve layer in order to stimulate the rods and cones.

In the area of the fovea each cone is connected to its own individual nerve, whereas in other regions of the retina up to 100 receptors may be feeding impulses into a single nerve fibre. This, and the close packing of the cones, accounts for the fine detail which is observed when images fall on the fovea. The fovea is further adapted to providing fine detail, as it is not covered by the curtain of blood vessels that are present over the rest of the retina.

The rods are extremely sensitive to light, and thus are responsible for **scotopic** vision (when the light intensity is low, such as in moonlight). However, they only ever give a simple perception of light, without any detail or colour.

The cones, by contrast, are responsible for **photopic** vision in ordinary bright conditions – for the perception of colour. Cones contain a yellowish pigment, which is why the fovea is known as the 'yellow spot'.

layer of each eyeball. The movement of both eyes is coordinated so that normally they converge simultaneously on the same point.

Figure 2.1 shows a vertical section through the eyeball, and Table 2.1 gives the description and purpose of each of the major component structures.

Each eyeball is roughly spherical in shape, with a diameter of ~25 mm. The lens–retina distance is ~20 mm, with the lens having an overall thickness of ~3.6 mm.

The retina

The retina is an important and complex part of the visual system that will now be dealt with in more detail.

Vision

We 'see' with our brain, as the actual image formed on the retina is real but upside down, and is slightly different for both eyes. The brain inverts and merges the two images to form a single upright impression of the object with perspective and contour, as Figure 2.3 shows.

One advantage of this two-image system is that we can use the effects of apparent size and parallax to judge distance and speed quite accurately.

A second advantage is that we are not normally aware of the blank area in our vision caused by the blind spot, since it is compensated for by the use of two eyes constantly scanning the visual field. Small adjustments are made so that the image is not projected on the same part of the retina for more than a fraction of a second. In addition, the blind spot never coincides with an image on which we concentrate. That falls on the fovea.

A disadvantage with the two-image system is that if our brain functions are dulled, for example by alcohol, then we may indeed 'see double'!

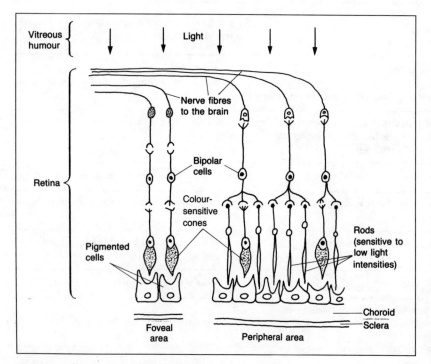

Figure 2.2   The sensory cells of the retina

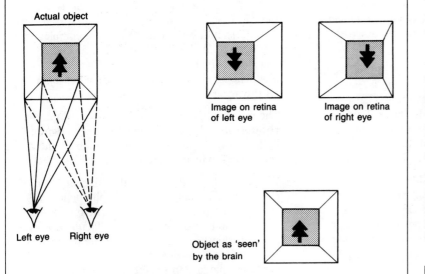

Figure 2.3   How we perceive depth

The lens makes the final adjustments to focus the image on the retina, a process called **accommodation**.

Accommodation

The lens can adjust the focus because of its natural elasticity, which enables it to change shape and hence focal length. These changes (Figure 2.5) are controlled by the ciliary muscles (circular and longitudinal) which are attached to the lens by the suspensory ligaments.

When viewing a distant object, the ciliary muscle is relaxed, and forms a circle of large diameter. This pulls the suspensory ligaments taut, which in turn pulls and flattens the lens, increasing its length (and decreasing its power).

Image formation

Figure 2.4 shows the actual process of image formation on the retina. It should be noted that the majority of the refraction necessary to focus the light on the retina takes place at the curved surface of the cornea, with the lens contributing only approximately a quarter of the total power of the optical system. This is because the greatest difference in refractive index occurs between the air and the cornea.

However, the cornea has a fixed focal length that would tend to focus the image either in front of or behind the retina, depending on the object position.

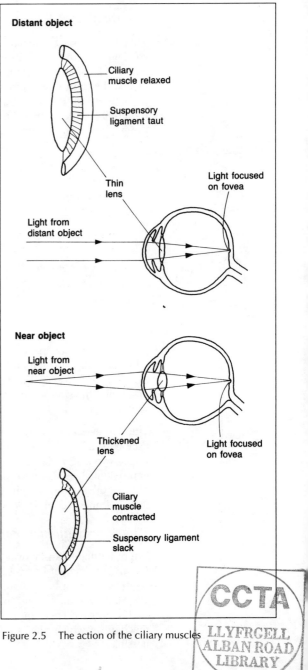

Figure 2.5   The action of the ciliary muscles

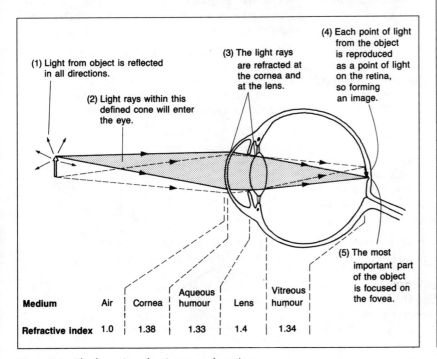

Medium	Air	Cornea	Aqueous humour	Lens	Vitreous humour
Refractive index	1.0	1.38	1.33	1.4	1.34

Figure 2.4   The formation of an image on the retina

In this condition the lens has its maximum focal length, and the normal eye will be able to focus quite clearly on objects from infinity down to approximately 5 metres.

When viewing an object nearer than this distance, the ciliary muscle contracts, making a circle of smaller diameter. This relaxes the suspensory ligaments, allowing the lens to bulge. This thicker lens has a shorter focal length (and higher power), allowing light from a close object to be brought to a focus on the retina.

A normal eye can accommodate a range of distances from infinity (the **far point**), down to a distance of approximately 25 cm in front of the eye (the **near point**), and has a power ranging from 50 D to 55 D (see page 13 for an explanation of power).

Control of light intensity

The amount of light reaching the retina is controlled by the iris. This is a thin circular disc formed of smooth muscle fibres arranged in two layers, the front one of circular fibres, the rear one of radial fibres. When the circular layers contract the pupil shrinks; when the radial layers contract the pupil dilates, as Figure 2.6 shows.

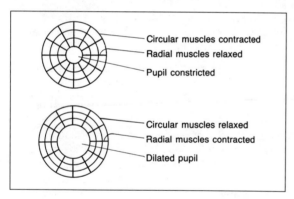

Figure 2.6   Control of pupil size by the iris

In this way the iris can control the amount of light entering the eye, as does the diaphragm of a camera. The size of the pupil varies in diameter from 2 mm to about 7.5 mm.

Sudden changes of light intensity falling upon the retina will cause the size of the pupil to alter – for instance the pupil will contract when walking out of a dark tunnel into bright sunlight. If, however, the light intensity varies gradually, the size of the pupil remains largely the same.

The two eyes are linked by nervous paths so that they both make the same adjustment no matter which eye is stimulated. Such adjustments take approximately 5 seconds to complete, and can alter the overall amount of light entering the eye by a factor of approximately 30.

Photosensitivity and adaptation

Bright sunlight can be over 10^5 times brighter than moonlight, and yet our eyes can still adapt to see relatively well in both conditions. Changes in pupil size alone cannot explain this ability to cope with such extremes. There must therefore be another mechanism which makes this adaptation process possible.

By far the major part of this adaptation is due to the variation in sensitivity of the retina itself. The actual mechanism of control is quite complex, but can be explained from the response of the retinal receptors, which depends on the magnitude of the photochemical effect which occurs when light falls on them.

The rods contain a pigment called visual purple, or **rhodopsin**, which is bleached by the action of light. It is this chemical change which produces the small e.m.f. which fires the nerve impulse.

When entering a dark place the concentration of rhodopsin is initially too low for photochemical effects to fire the nerve impulse. The rods are thus inactive, and vision is therefore difficult. However, more rhodopsin is generated and the photochemical effect increases, as does the visual response of the eye. This increase in sensitivity continues until there is equilibrium between the processes of decomposition and regeneration of the rhodopsin. The eye thus adapts to decreasing levels of illumination, a process known as **dark adaptation**. Dark adaptation is a continuous process, responding to different magnitudes of stimulation.

The cones, active only under bright conditions, contain a colourless photochemical substance called **iodopsin**. The cones adapt in a similar way to decreasing levels of bright light when they alone are active. This tends to happen more quickly than for the rods, indicating that iodopsin regenerates more quickly than rhodopsin.

In between dark and bright conditions, there is a range of illumination in which both cones and rods are active, as shown in Figure 2.7. The figure also shows why in poor light the ability to distinguish colour is reduced (weak cone response).

It is also worth noting that at low levels of illumination our peripheral vision is dominant (since rods predominate there), and we see a distinct outline with little other detail. In fact in poor light objects sometimes 'disappear' when

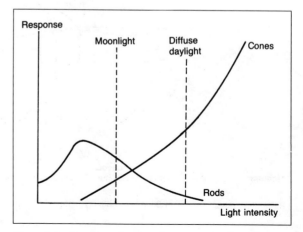

Figure 2.7   Reaction of rods and cones to different light intensities

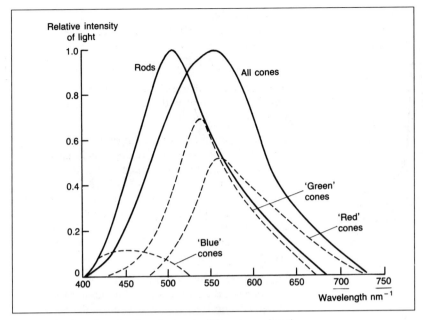

Figure 2.8   Reaction of rods and cones to different wavelengths

Discrimination between these different wavelengths is achieved by three principal types of cones. Although all these are sensitive to all the visual wavelengths, each one is particularly sensitive to a different part of the spectrum. One type is particularly sensitive to red, one to green and one to blue. The stimulation of these different receptors by varying degrees is combined by the brain to give the perception of the whole spectrum of colour.

This situation is similar to colour television, where the whole range of colours is produced by stimulating only the three primary colour phosphors.

The sensitivities of the 'red', 'green' and 'blue' cones vary considerably with wavelength, so that equal intensities of different wavelengths will in general produce different sensations of brightness. As can be seen from Figure 2.8, all the cones are sensitive in some measure to the blue-green part of the spectrum. Thus, adding the three cone responses together gives an overall sensitivity peak for colour vision at 555 nm (yellow-green).

The rods are also sensitive to light over the whole of the visible spectrum, but have greatest sensitivity at approximately 510 nm (blue-green) and least sensitivity in the red part of the spectrum. However, since the rods have no colour discrimination, the magnitude of their response to different wavelengths is only perceived as more or less light, i.e. shades of grey.

The stimulation of both rods and cones gives a peak sensitivity in the middle of the visible spectrum, which thus appears brighter than either the red or blue ends.

In poor light a greater proportion of the light sensitivity will be due to the action of the rods than of the cones. Since the rods are more sensitive to blue-green light, there is a shift in maximum sensitivity with decreasing illumination towards this end of the spectrum. This is responsible for the relatively dark appearance of red objects under low levels of illumination. For this reason many road signs use blue or green backgrounds.

The smallest wavelength difference that is just detectable as a difference of colour also varies over the different wavelengths of the spectrum. It ranges between 1 nm and 6 nm, as shown in Figure 2.9.

This discriminatory ability improves as the size of the visual field increases.

looked at directly, since the image then falls on the cone-rich fovea.

Light adaptation is the reverse of dark adaptation; the eye becomes less sensitive to light due to a reduction in the concentration of the photochemical substances. Light adaptation occurs more quickly than dark adaptation, which explains why the eyes can take only a few minutes to adjust to bright sunlight, but up to 30 minutes to gain good night vision.

Spectral response

The eye is generally sensitive to electromagnetic radiation of wavelengths in the range 380–760 nm.

Persistence of vision

When a visual stimulus is suddenly removed, the sensation it produced on the retina takes a finite time to disappear. The time for which this **after-image** is 'seen' varies considerably with the conditions of adaptation and the strength and duration of the stimulus. In bright light it can take ~0.02 s to fade completely, whereas in dim light

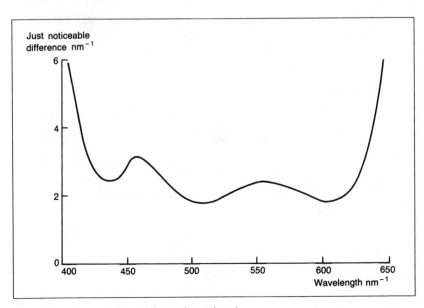

Figure 2.9   Discriminatory ability and wavelength

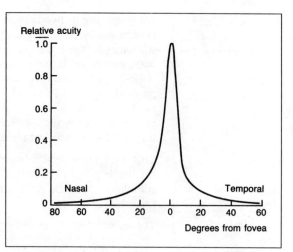

Figure 2.10   Visual acuity over different areas of the retina

$$\theta = 1.22\lambda/d$$

where λ is $\sim 5 \times 10^{-7}$ m (approximate peak response wavelength)

and $d = 2 \times 10^{-3}$ m (smallest diameter of the pupil)

This gives a resolving power of ~1 minute of arc, which is consistent with the angle subtended at the pupil by a single cell on the retina.

The accuracy of the brain's impression of the image received by the eye therefore depends largely on how numerous and closely packed are the retinal receptors. Since each one can only record the presence or absence of a point of light (and in the case of cones, its colour), it is reasonable to assume that if the 'eye' is to resolve two neighbouring retinal images, there must be an unstimulated receptor between them.

Figure 2.10 shows that the spatial resolution of the eye, or **visual acuity**, is therefore greatest when an image falls on the fovea, since this is the area of highest receptor density.

In bright light, as one moves away from the fovea, the visual acuity decreases rapidly due to the decreased resolving ability of the retina. In dim light the fovea is inactive, and then the region just beyond it gives maximum acuity.

the after-image lasts for up to 0.2 s, as rods respond less quickly to change than do cones.

Without this 'persistence of vision', when watching cine films and television we would be aware of each individual frame which makes up the 'moving' image, usually running at 25 frames per second. On older films, running at fewer frames per second, this 'flicker' is quite noticeable.

Persistence of vision can also cause colour-based effects. If, for example, a moderately dark-adapted (sensitive) eye looks at a strong white light, the after-image often changes colour through red, green and blue, becoming less definite in form.

In addition, if you look at a strong source of one colour, then suddenly look at a weakly illuminated white screen, the after-image is seen in a complementary colour to the original stimulus. In this way it is actually possible to see a pink elephant – by looking first at a cyan-coloured example!

Spatial resolution

Resolving power is defined as the minimum angular separation θ (in radians) for which two objects can be distinguished as separate. It is given by the equation:

Depth of field and depth of focus

When the eye is correctly focused, the lens brings light rays to a point on the retina. In front of and behind this retinal plane it projects not a point but a circle, the 'circle of confusion', whose size increases with distance from the focal plane. However, the smallest circles of confusion may still give a sharp enough image to be perceived as 'in focus'. There is thus a small distance on either side of the retina before the image becomes noticeably blurred. This distance is called the **depth of focus**.

The **depth of field** is the corresponding distance through which an object can be moved and still produce an 'in focus' image.

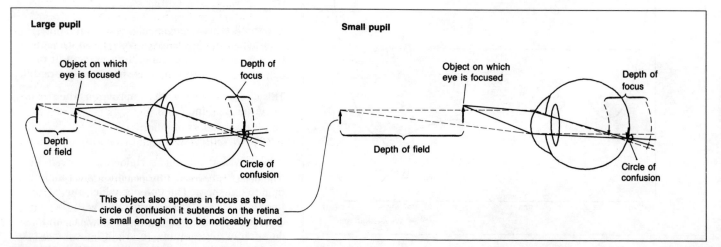

Figure 2.11   Relation of depth of field and pupil size

The depth of focus (and hence depth of field) is dependent on the size of the pupil, as shown in Figure 2.11. The smaller the pupil, the greater the depth of focus. This is because the circle of confusion then increases in size less quickly. It is analogous to the camera, where a small aperture produces a large depth of focus or field.

Depth of field must not be confused with **field of vision**, which indicates the zone that can be seen simultaneously with the head kept stationary, as shown in Figure 2.12.

Humans can see objects within an angle of approximately 200°, though only objects within an angle of approximately 2° will form an image on

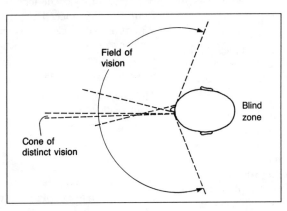

Figure 2.12
Field of vision

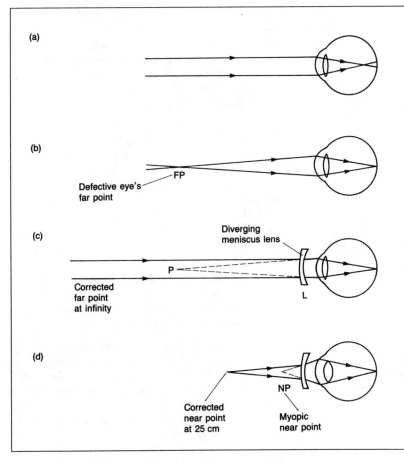

Figure 2.13   Correction of myopia

the fovea and so be seen in accurate detail. The exact field of view depends on the shape of the face, but extends laterally beyond 90° on the temporal side, and over 60° on the nasal side. It extends vertically approximately 50° upwards and 70° downwards.

Defects of vision

Before looking at defects of vision and their methods of correction, we should examine the various terms that we use to define 'normal vision'.

The **visual axis** is the line joining the fovea and the so-called fixation point. This does not coincide exactly with the optical axis, but for our purposes this assumption will be made.

The **visual angle** is the angle subtended at the eye by the object. It is dependent on both the size of the object and its distance from the eye. It determines the size of the image formed on the retina, and hence how large we perceive the object to be.

The **far point** (normally infinity) and **near point** were discussed on page 8. The distance from the eye to the near point is called the **least distance of distinct vision**. It is usually taken to be 25 cm, but increases with age.

The **power of accommodation** is the maximum change in power (due to the lens) of which the eye is capable. (The power of an optical system in dioptres is defined on page 13.) For the 'average person' this may vary from ~14 dioptres at 10 years old to 4 dioptres at age 40, and almost zero at age 75.

Defects of vision may occur either because the lens cannot accommodate the power of the optical system, or because of a fault in the geometry of the eyeball.

Short sight, or myopia

Short-sighted (**myopic**) people can only see near objects clearly – distant objects are blurred. The condition occurs either because the eyeball is too long, or because the optical system is too powerful even when the eye lens is fully relaxed. In both cases light from a distant object is brought to a focus in front of the retina (Figure 2.13(a)).

Distant objects cannot thus be brought to a sharp focus on the retina, and the eye's far point (FP) is considerably short of infinity (Figure 2.13(b)). The near point (NP) is also usually abnormally close to the eye, but this is not detrimental to vision.

The defect is corrected by placing a diverging (concave) spherical lens in front of the eye. The power of the lens is chosen so that parallel light is diverged by such an amount as to appear to have come from a 'virtual object' placed at the defective eye's own far point (Figure 2.13(c)). This virtual object is in fact the upright virtual image which would be formed by the spectacle lens if used alone. As may be seen from Figure 2.13(c), the focal length of the required lens is equal to the distance PL, which is almost the same as the distance from the far point of the eye. Lenses for myopic sufferers are thus generally of long focal length.

Since the overall power of the optical system (eye + spectacle lens) has now been reduced to a 'normal' level, the accommodation of the eye's own lens is capable of focusing any object between infinity and the near point. As can be seen from Figure 2.13(d), the near point is now slightly further from the eye than it was without the spectacles, but it is still within the 'normal' least distance of distinct vision.

The spectacles, for convenience, can thus be worn at all times, but are not essential for close work. The chosen lens is usually meniscus shaped, to fit the curvature of the eye. If contact lenses are used, the lens shape must accurately fit the curvature of the cornea.

One very recent development provides the first real alternative to corrective lenses, whether as spectacles or contact lenses. This uses a precision-guided laser, directed by computer, to vaporise parts of the cornea, thus correcting the vision defect (more information on lasers can be found in Chapter 6). If the promise of the early research work is fulfilled in clinical practice, this will provide an exciting development.

Long sight, or hypermetropia

Hypermetropic or long-sighted eyes can only see distant objects clearly. The near (and far) points are both further away than in the 'normal' eye (Figure 2.14(a)).

The condition occurs either because the eyeball is too short, or because the optical system is too weak, even when the eye is fully accommodated, so that light from close objects cannot be refracted sufficiently, and hence the image would be formed beyond the retina (Figure 2.14(b)).

Long sight is corrected by using a converging (convex) spherical lens to increase the refractive power of the eye. The lens is chosen such that rays from an object placed at the normal near point of 25 cm are converged by such an amount that they appear to have come from the person's actual near point (Figure 2.14(c)). The eye lens is then able to focus this virtual image.

The effect of such a spectacle lens on the eye's far point is likely to merely bring it back to infinity, so once again the spectacles can be worn at all times.

Presbyopia

Whereas long and short sight are defects of refraction, **presbyopia** is a defect of accommodation normally associated with age.

It occurs because as a person gets older, calcium is deposited in the lens, causing it to lose its elasticity. This results in a reduction in the power of accommodation to less than 4 dioptres. The effect on vision is that neither distant nor close objects can be seen clearly, although the change in the far point is usually much less than the change in the near point.

If the change in the far point is not noticeable, correction may only be needed to reduce the defective eye's near point back to ~25 cm by using a converging spectacle lens, as in long sight. However, this would also have the effect of bringing the far point closer, as shown in Figure 2.15(a). Such spectacles would therefore only be used for reading and close work.

If correction is needed for both the near and far point, this results in the use of two pairs of spectacles, or a pair of **bifocals**. Bifocals contain an upper diverging lens for clear vision of distant objects (as in short sight), and a lower converging lens for close work (Figure 2.15(b)).

It is important to realise that in all cases of defective vision, the correcting lens must be such that it produces a *virtual upright image* of the object at the defective eye's own near or far point. The defective eye's refracting system is then able to cope and produce a focused image on the retina. A real image cannot be produced by the spectacle lens, as this would interfere with the light from the actual object being looked at.

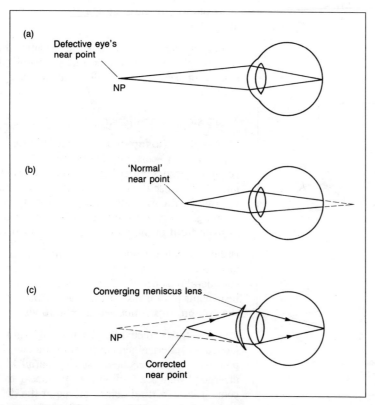

Figure 2.14   Correction of hypermetropia

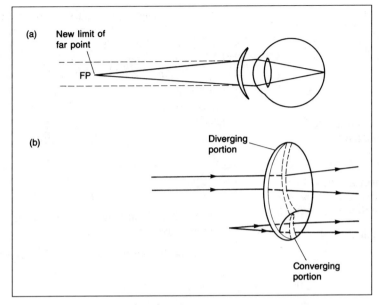

Figure 2.15   Correction of presbyopia

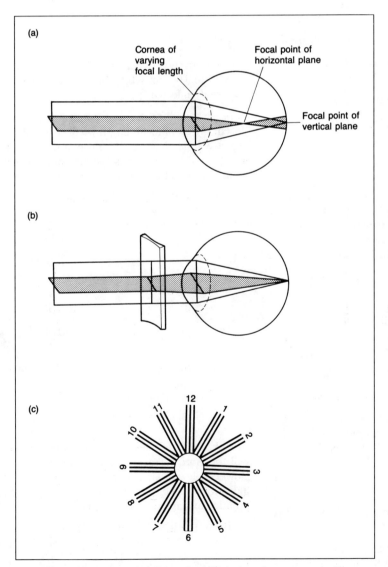

Figure 2.16   (a) Uncorrected astigmatism (b) Astigmatism corrected with a cylindrical lens (c) Test for astigmatism

Astigmatism

Astigmatism is a defect which arises when the cornea is not exactly spherical in shape. This variation in the radius of curvature results in the eye having a different focal length in various planes (Figure 2.16(a)).

Astigmatism is corrected by using a cylindrical spectacle lens whose curvature compensates for the abnormal curvature of the cornea (Figure 2.16 (b)). The angle at which the lens is fitted into the frame must be specified as it depends on the direction in which the astigmastic effects occur.

Figure 2.16(c) shows a typical diagram used in the diagnosis of astigmatism. To the normal eye the three lines at each angle are all distinct, but to the astigmatic eye one or more sets may be blurred because the rays of light from that direction will not be focused onto the retinal surface at the same time.

Colour blindness

The most common form of colour blindness is the inability to distinguish between red and green. It is probably caused by a deficiency of one of the types of cone normally present in the retina. Approximately 8% of men and 0.5% of women suffer from some form of colour blindness.

Tests for colour blindness are made using charts of coloured dots (Ishihara and Stilling–Hertel charts). The dots are of the same brightness, but two colours are used (say red and green). A number is depicted in one of the colours. If the number cannot be perceived by the eye, then the person is colour blind. By varying the brightness of the colours, the degree of sensitivity to colour, as well as the total absence of sensitivity, can be determined.

Calculations for correcting vision defects

Refracting power

The refracting power of a surface is defined by:

$$\text{Power in dioptres (D)} = \frac{1}{\text{focal length in metres}}$$

$$P = \frac{1}{f}$$

If the focal length f is in cm, then power, $P = \frac{100}{f}$

The powers of compound systems can be added together algebraically, often to give a more meaningful quantity than the focal lengths of the constituent parts. The overall power of the eye is usually between 60 D and 70 D.

Myopia

Consider a short-sighted person whose far point is reduced to a distance of only 100 cm from the eye. The near point is at 18 cm.

Using the lens formula:
(real is positive convention) $\dfrac{1}{f} = \dfrac{1}{u} + \dfrac{1}{v}$

where u is the object distance, v the image distance, f the focal length of the lens.

The object is placed at infinity, i.e. $u = \infty$

Now the spectacle lens must form a virtual image of this object which will be at the person's actual far point. The image distance is therefore 100 cm.

So $v = -100$, the minus sign indicating that the image is virtual.

Substituting: $\dfrac{1}{f} = \dfrac{1}{\infty} - \dfrac{1}{100}$

$= 0 - \dfrac{1}{100}$

Therefore: $f = -100$ cm

The minus sign indicates that the lens is diverging.

A concave lens of focal length 100 cm is therefore required to correct the defect.

The power of the lens in dioptres is given by:

$$P = \frac{100}{f}$$

Therefore, power of correcting lens $= -1$ D

To find the effect of this lens on the person's near point we again apply the lens formula. The object is now placed at a distance u which will produce a virtual image at the defective near point of 18 cm. Therefore $v = -18$ and $f = -100$ (a situation similar to Figure 2.13(d)).

Substituting in the
lens formula: $\dfrac{-1}{100} = \dfrac{1}{u} - \dfrac{1}{18}$

Therefore: $\dfrac{1}{u} = \dfrac{1}{18} - \dfrac{1}{100}$

$= 0.046$

And so: u $= 21.9$ cm

The person's near point when wearing the spectacles has receded to ~22 cm, but is still closer than normal. The range of distinct vision has been enormously increased.

Hypermetropia

Consider a long-sighted person whose near point is at a distance of 50 cm.

A suitable lens to bring the near point back to the normal distance of 25 cm can be found by applying the lens formula.

As can be seen from Figure 2.14(c), an object placed at the normal near point of 25 cm must produce a virtual image at the least distance of distinct vision for that person. Therefore $u = 25$ cm and $v = -50$ cm (the minus sign again indicating a virtual image).

Substituting in the
lens formula: $\dfrac{1}{f} = \dfrac{1}{25} - \dfrac{1}{50}$

$= \dfrac{1}{50}$

$f = 50$ cm

A convex lens of focal length 50 cm is thus required to correct the defect.

The power of the required lens would be given by:

$$P = \frac{100}{f}$$

$$= \frac{100}{50}$$

$$= +2 \text{ D}$$

Presbyopia

Consider an ageing person whose near point has receded to 100 cm whilst her far point is not noticeably affected.

In order to reduce the near point to the normal 25 cm a lens of focal length f will be required. An object will be placed at the normal near point, i.e. $u = 25$ cm, but the virtual image must appear to be at the actual near point, so $v = -100$ cm

Applying the lens formula again:

$\dfrac{1}{f} = \dfrac{1}{u} + \dfrac{1}{v}$

$= \dfrac{1}{25} - \dfrac{1}{100}$

$= \dfrac{3}{100}$

Or: $f = \dfrac{100}{3}$

Therefore: $f = 33.3$ cm

And: $P = \dfrac{100}{f}$

$= +3$ D

A convex lens of power +3 D (focal length 33.3 cm) will therefore correct the defect in the near point. However, it will also alter the far point such that light from an object at the new far point will now produce an image at infinity, i.e. $v = \infty$.

Using the lens formula: $\dfrac{1}{f} = \dfrac{1}{u} + \dfrac{1}{v}$

$\dfrac{1}{33.3} = \dfrac{1}{u} + \dfrac{1}{\infty}$

$$\frac{1}{u} = \frac{1}{33.3}$$

Therefore: $u = 33.3$ cm

i.e. the far point has been reduced to only 33.3 cm. Wearing the glasses therefore means that the range of distinct vision is only 8.3 cm!

Machines used to examine the eye

The **ophthalmoscope** (Figure 2.17) is an inexpensive tool for examining the eye. It has a strong light source which is directed into the patient's eye by reflection from a small mirror.

The light is reflected from the back of the patient's eye through a small slit in the mirror, and into the eye of the examining clinician. If both the clinician's and the patient's eyes are normal, and the clinician is close to the patient, the patient's inner eye will be in focus. If this is not the case, small lenses can be rotated into the path until focusing occurs. Lesions in the cornea, opacity of the eye lens and detachment of the retina are some of the typical disorders which can be seen with the aid of the ophthalmoscope.

A **tonometer** is used to measure intraocular pressure – the pressure of the humours keeping the eyeball's shape. Increases of pressure from the normal range can be the result of glaucoma. If left unattended this can lead to the destruction of some bundles of nerve fibres, or of the blood supply to the retina. Both conditions can result in blindness.

An **ultrasound A-scanner** (see Chapter 13, pages 111–12) is used to determine the intraocular distances. It achieves this by measuring the time taken for a beam of ultrasound, directed from a probe into the eye, to be reflected from the various structures within the eye back to a detector. One of

its uses is to determine the power of a replacement lens used when the eye's natural lens is removed because of cataracts.

A **field analyser** is used to test the field of vision of a patient – the area which can be seen without moving the eye. This usually consists of a sphere of spots which can be illuminated from behind. The operator illuminates them in turn and asks the patient to tell when they can be seen.

A **retinal camera** can photograph the retina through the iris using an infrared filter. The pattern of blood vessels within the eye can then be seen, as can any retinal detachment or haemorrhages into the vitreous humour from the retinal vessels.

Questions

1. a) Draw a diagram to illustrate long sight (hypermetropia) and a second diagram showing its correction by means of a suitable lens.

    Without spectacles an elderly person has a normal far point but is unable to see clearly objects closer than 200 cm.

    i) Find the power in dioptres of the spectacle lens which alters the near point to 25 cm.
    ii) Find the far point and calculate the range of distinct vision when the person is wearing the spectacles.

    b) Explain with the aid of a diagram the term **depth of focus** applied to the human eye.

    An object at a fixed distance from the eye is viewed when the pupil is i) large and ii) small. State and explain which condition gives rise to the larger depth of focus, supporting your answer by means of a diagram.

    c) A person with normal eyesight observes a bright light which flashes for 0.020 s at intervals of 10 s. Explain how the person's perception of the bright light changes as the intervals are progressively reduced and name the effect which is responsible. State *one* practical application of the effect.

2. a) i) State the nature of the defect known as astigmatism and name the type of lens used to correct it.

    ii) An old person and a young person each wear spectacles with converging lenses. In *each* case name the probable eye defect, stating its nature and how correction is achieved.

    b) The combined power of cornea and lens of a normal, unaccommodated eye is 59 dioptres. If the eye focuses on an object 250 mm away find the change in power, in dioptres, of the eye.

3. A myopic eye has a far point of 1.0 m and a near point of 150 mm. State the type of spectacle lens needed for viewing an object at the normal far point and determine its power, in dioptres. Find the near point when wearing this lens.

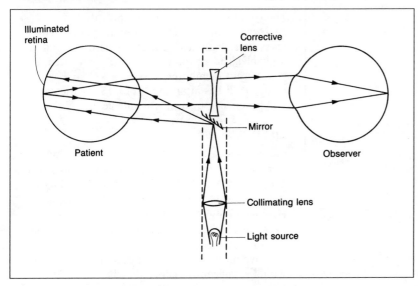

Illuminated retina

Corrective lens

Mirror

Patient

Observer

Collimating lens

Light source

Figure 2.17   The ophthalmoscope

3 HEARING

Transmission and characteristics of sound

The function of the ear is to transmit to the brain an accurate representation of the sound vibrations that it picks up from the environment.

Sound is a longitudinal pressure wave propagated through a medium by means of small oscillations of the particles of that medium. The distance between two successive pressure maxima (or minima) is the **wavelength** λ of that wave. The **frequency** f is related to the wavelength by the formula $v = f\lambda$, where v is the speed of propagation of the wave. The frequency is characteristic of the original source of the sound wave.

The maximum displacement of any individual particle from its mean position as the wave travels through the medium is the **amplitude** of the wave.

The **intensity** of the sound is a measure of the rate of transfer of energy away from the source. The intensity of a sound:

* at a particular point is defined as the energy flowing per second through 1 square metre in a plane at right angles to the direction of propagation of the sound;
* decreases as the square of the distance r from the source;
* at a given frequency is directly proportional to the square of the amplitude of the wave.

The characteristics of sound depend on these properties of the wave motion:

* pitch – dependent on frequency;
* loudness – dependent on intensity and frequency;
* quality, or timbre – dependent on the range of frequencies present, and their relative amplitudes.

The structure of the ear

The ear is divided into three main parts – the outer, middle and inner ears, separated by thin membranes or 'windows' through which the sound waves travel. Figure 3.1 shows the structure of the ear.

The outer ear

The outer ear comprises the visible part known as the pinna or auricle, and an S-shaped tube or canal called the external auditory meatus. The pinna consists of irregularly shaped fibrous tissue which is only very slightly moveable. It funnels sound into the 2.5 cm-long canal towards the eardrum or tympanic membrane.

The canal is directed slightly upwards and backwards, and is lined with many glands whose waxy secretions help protect the eardrum and keep it pliable. The 'drum' itself is a thin stretched semi-transparent membrane of skin, less than 1 cm in diameter. It lies at an angle of ~45° to the canal and is concave towards the middle ear.

The middle ear

The middle ear or tympanic cavity is a small (0.6 cm³) air-filled chamber which lies between the eardrum and the bone surrounding the inner ear. If the tympanic cavity was completely enclosed, changes in atmospheric pressure such as we experience in lifts and aeroplanes would cause a pressure difference across the eardrum, causing it to move more in one direction than another. This would significantly reduce the efficiency of the transmission of the sound.

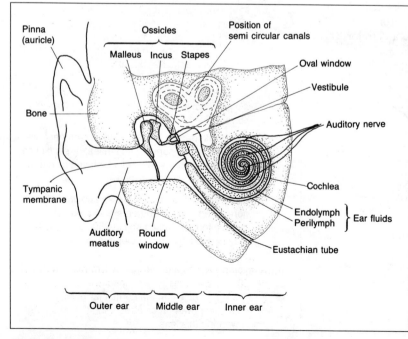

Figure 3.1   Structure of the ear

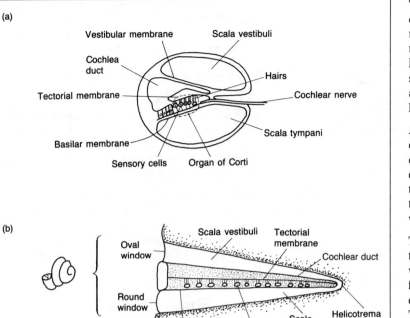

Figure 3.2
(a) Section through the cochlea
(b) The cochlea uncoiled

The cochlea is a spiral tube curled up in the shape of a snail's shell with $2\frac{5}{8}$ turns. The diameter of this tube decreases from the point at which it joins the vestibule to its central apex, called the helicotrema. A cross-section of the cochlea is shown in Figure 3.2(a), with a longitudinal section as it would be if it were opened out shown in Figure 3.2(b).

As can be seen from the diagrams, the spiral canal of the cochlea is divided into two passages by the cochlear duct throughout the length of the canal, except at the apex. These two passages known as the scala vestibuli and the scala tympani. (In effect there are three adjoining tubes which spiral round, with two of them joining at the apex.)

The scala vestibuli is connected at its base end to the oval window, and the scala tympani connects with the round window. Both are filled with a clear fluid known as perilymph. They communicate with each other via a small opening at the central apex. This opening is too small to allow the rapid movement of the fluid between the passages during vibrations.

The cochlear duct is the smallest of the three channels, and is filled with another clear fluid known as endolymph. It is separated from the upper scala vestibuli by the thin vestibular membrane, and from the lower scala tympani by a tougher basilar membrane.

The basilar membrane is made up of reed-like fibres which can vibrate at particular frequencies. Near to the base of the membrane the fibres are short and stiff, and vibrate at high frequencies. Nearer the apex the fibres are long and more flexible, and vibrate at lower frequencies.

Resting on the basilar membrane is a single layer of sensory cells, approximately 30 000 in number, with fine hairs projecting from their free upper edge into the endolymph. The hairs are also connected to a gelatinous ribbon called the tectorial membrane. These hairs, together with their supporting cells, are known as the organ of Corti, and constitute the hearing receptors which direct nervous impulses through the auditory nerve to the brain.

To prevent this happening, a narrow passage called the eustachian tube connects the middle ear via the nasal passages to the atmosphere. If the external pressure on the eardrum changes, the muscles of the eustachian tube open to release air from or into the middle ear, equalising the pressure again.

Within the middle ear, suspended by ligaments, are three interconnecting bones or ossicles known as the hammer (malleus), anvil (incus) and stirrup (stapes), because of their shapes. These bones are arranged across the middle ear like a chain, reaching from the eardrum to the inner ear. The 'handle' of the hammer is attached to the inner surface of the eardrum. Its other end is connected, via a joint, to the anvil, which in turn is connected to the stirrup. The footplate of the stirrup is attached to the oval window. This, and a second membrane called the round window, separate the middle and inner ears.

The inner ear

The fluid-filled inner ear is a complex bony chamber located within the temporal bone of the skull. It comprises the semicircular canals, the vestibule and the cochlea.

There are three semicircular canals at right angles to each other, called the superior, posterior and lateral canals. The semicircular canals are part of the system of balance and play no part in the hearing mechanism.

The vestibule is the central cavity with which all the other parts communicate. It lies between the oval window and the cochlea.

The mechanism of hearing

As Figure 3.3 shows, sound waves entering the outer ear are directed by the funnel shape of the pinna into the canal. The latter serves as a resonator which increases the pressure changes and hence the intensity of the vibrations, channelling them towards the eardrum. The funnelling causes an increase in intensity within the outer ear by a factor of 10–20 for frequencies between 1500 Hz and 7000 Hz. These pressure changes in the sound waves are then transferred into small ($\sim 10^{-11}$ m) *transverse* vibrations of the eardrum.

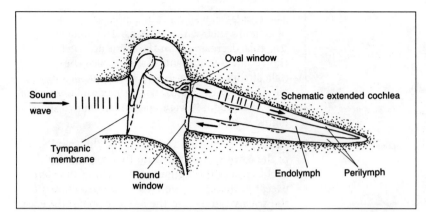

Fgiure 3.3   The mechanism of hearing

Acting as a series of levers, the three ossicles then conduct the vibrations from the eardrum to the oval window.

The leverage effect of the ossicles is such that the ratio of the force exerted on the malleus to that exerted by the stapes is 1:1.3. In addition, the effective area of the tympanic membrane is 65 mm², and the effective area of the oval window is 3.2 mm². The combined effect of this is that the pressure is increased as sound travels from the eardrum to the oval window, first by the factor of 1.3, and then by a factor of 20 (= 65/3.2), giving a total pressure increase of 26.

The resulting vibrations of the oval window cause a longitudinal pressure wave to travel through the perilymph of the scala vestibuli. Since fluids are not compressible, the resultant changes in pressure in this upper compartment are transmitted across the cochlear duct to the lower scala tympani, from where they pass to the round window. The vibrations of the round window therefore coincide with those received by the oval window, but are in antiphase (and slightly delayed).

The distortion of the cochlear duct which results from the pressure differences in the vestibular and tympanic compartments causes a displacement of the basilar membrane relative to the tectorial membrane. The resultant movement of the cilia

hairs causes a change in the electrical potential across them, and thus a current flows in the nerve fibres to the brain via the auditory nerve. Figure 3.4 shows this schematically.

Transmission of sound through bone

Because the cochlea is embedded in a bony cavity, vibrations of the skull can cause vibrations in the cochlea fluids. A tuning fork or electric vibrator placed on the bony protrusion called the mastoid process and vibrating at the appropriate frequency will result in sound being heard.

When we speak, we hear own own voices partially through air conduction, and partially through bone conduction. As a result, when we hear a recording of our voice it can sound very different, as the sound on the recording has been detected solely through air conduction.

Stereophonic hearing

Our two ears provide us with stereophonic hearing so that we can judge the direction of a sound. This is possible because both ears receive 'sounds' from a stationary source differing in three respects: intensity, phase and time lag.

If the source of a sound is off to one side, then it will be heard more loudly by one ear than the other. A short, sharp sound, also off to one side, will be heard slightly earlier by one ear than the other. If the sound is continuous, then the phase difference of the wave as it is received by each ear will produce out-of-phase impulses in the auditory nerve, which again will help the brain in interpreting the position of the source.

If the source is equidistant from both ears, it is more difficult to locate its position since both ears are stimulated equally. It is also difficult to distinguish between two identical sounds which are less than 45° apart, due to diffraction effects. This is most noticeable with low frequencies.

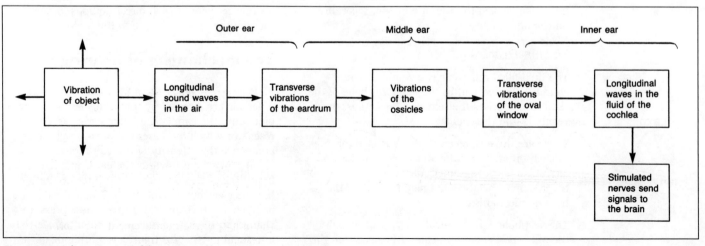

Figure 3.4   Schematic view of the process of hearing

Frequency response

There is a considerable individual variation in the **frequency range** to which the human ear responds. The lowest frequency that can be heard is ~20 Hz (lower frequencies are generally felt rather than heard!). The upper frequency limit varies considerably with age. For young children it can be as high as 30 000 Hz (30 kHz), but this decreases rapidly to ~20 kHz at maturity, and falls further with age to ~15 kHz. The greatest sensitivity occurs in the range 1–4 kHz – the curve of audibility showing the absolute threshold for different frequencies dips to its lowest point within the 1–4 kHz range, as Figure 3.5 shows.

Frequency discrimination is the ear's ability to distinguish one frequency from another. It varies considerably with the original frequency, and is much greater at low frequencies. In the range 60 Hz–1 kHz the ear can distinguish differences in pitch corresponding to ~3 Hz. This discriminant ability decreases as the frequency increases, and above 10 kHz frequency discrimination is almost non-existent.

The mechanism by which we perceive sound to be of different frequency (pitch) is not fully understood, but is thought to depend on which parts of the basilar membrane are stimulated. High frequencies act on the shorter fibres of the membrane near the oval window, whilst the lower frequencies penetrate further down the cochlea to activate the longer fibres near the apex (Figure 3.6). The brain thus determines pitch by detecting which section of the organ of Corti has been stimulated.

The positional theory does not completely explain the method of distinguishing frequency, for the far end of the basilar membrane is stimulated by all frequencies below 200 Hz, and yet it is possible for the ear to distinguish between these frequencies. At present the secondary mechanism which enables this further discrimination is not known, but it is thought that at low frequencies the cochlea sends out volleys of impulses at the same low frequencies into the cochlear nerves.

Intensity and the decibel scale

The range of intensities or pressure changes which the ear can distinguish is very large. If one unit of intensity is the smallest amount which can be detected by the ear, then the greatest intensity which can be detected before the ear is damaged is 10^{15} times as large. This range of intensities is known as the **dynamic range**.

Because of the very wide dynamic range of the ear, the determination of relative intensities in hearing cannot easily use the most common, interval scale, where the distance between each successive number is equal. Another type of scale is the ratio scale, in which the ratio of any two successive numbers in the scale is constant. One example of a ratio scale is 10, 100, 1000, 10 000, ..., in which the ratio of any two successive numbers is 1:10. This type of scale, often referred to as a logarithmic scale, is used in hearing.

To illustrate the compression that a logarithmic scale gives, let us take the numbers 10 and 1 000 000.

The theory of logarithms says that:

Since $1 = 10^0$,   then $\log 1 = 0$
Since $10 = 10^1$,   then $\log 10 = 1$
Since $100 = 10^2$, then $\log 100 = 2$

and in general: $\log 10^n = n$

Going back to our illustration, the use of a logarithmic scale has allowed us to compress the wide range from 10 to 1 000 000 to a scale of 1–6.

The unit of sound measurement based on this type of logarithmic scale is the bel, and is defined such that for two sources of intensity I and I_o:

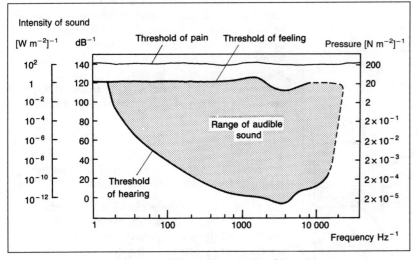

Figure 3.5   Response of the ear to different frequencies and intensities

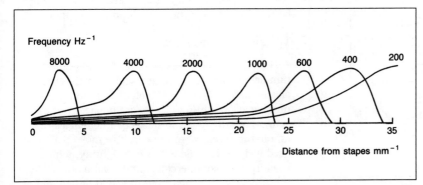

Figure 3.6   Distance travelled along the organ of Corti by sounds of different pitch

$$\text{Intensity level} = \log_{10} \frac{I}{I_o} \text{ bel}$$

In practice the bel is too large a unit to be useful and the decibel or **dB** is used, where 1 bel = 10 dB.

Hence:

$$\text{Intensity level} = 10 \times \log_{10} \frac{I}{I_o} \text{ dB}$$

So, if the intensity of the sound doubles from I to $2I$, then:

$$\text{Intensity level} = 10 \times \log_{10} \frac{2I}{I_o}$$

$$= 10 \times \log_{10}(2) + 10 \times \log_{10} \frac{I}{I_o}$$

$$\begin{aligned}\text{Thus the change}\\ \text{in intensity level}\end{aligned} = 10 \times \log_{10}(2) \text{ dB}$$

$$= 10 \times 0.301 \text{ dB}$$

$$\approx 3 \text{ dB}$$

Using the above logarithmic calculation, if the sound intensity increases by a factor of 10, the change in intensity level will be: $10 \times \log_{10} 10 = 10$ dB.

The dynamic range of hearing as expressed in the original system was $1-10^{15}$. Using the logarithmic intensity scale of the decibel system this converts to a range of 0–150 dB.

The 'zero' level, or **reference intensity** I_o is usually taken as 10^{-12} W m^{-2}.

Sound pressure levels

In some cases the pressure of the sound wave is used rather than the intensity.

As sound pressure $P \propto I^2$, where I is intensity:

$$\text{Sound pressure level} = 10 \log_{10} \left[\frac{P}{P_o}\right]^2 \text{ dB}$$

$$= 20 \log_{10} \frac{P}{P_o} \text{ dB}$$

where P_o is the reference sound pressure, usually taken as 2×10^{-5} Pa.

Loudness

The intensity or pressure of a sound wave is independent of the observer, whereas the **loudness** of a sound is a measure of sensation and depends not only on the intensity of the sound but also on the hearing of the observer.

The loudness of a sound is detected by the auditory system in several different ways. Firstly, for an increase in sound amplitude there is a corresponding increase in the amplitude of the vibration of the basilar membrane which causes an increase in the excitation of the hair cells. Secondly, as the amplitude of vibration of the membrane increases, more hair cells near to the resonating part of the basilar membrane are stimulated. As the sound becomes louder still, certain hair cells not normally stimulated are excited.

The phon

A number of scales have been used to 'measure' loudness. One such scale is the **phon**.

The phon is based on a series of 'equal loudness curves', shown in Figure 3.7, constructed by determining the sound pressure levels necessary for a tone of any given frequency to have the same loudness as a 1 kHz tone. Thus, as lower frequencies do not sound as loud as the 1 kHz reference tone, a higher sound pressure level will be required to give the same loudness in phons.

Weighted sound levels

A similar approach has been used to obtain a number of different loudness scales. In these scales, classed as A-, B-, C- or D-weighted scales, a number of weighting factors are applied to the sound pressure levels at different frequencies to mimic the response of the ear. The most commonly used weighting scale is the A-weighting, which is used in most commercial sound level meters. The sound levels thus measured are then designated as measured in dB(A).

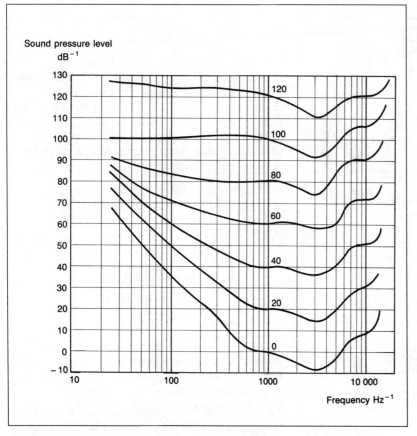

Figure 3.7   The phon scale of loudness

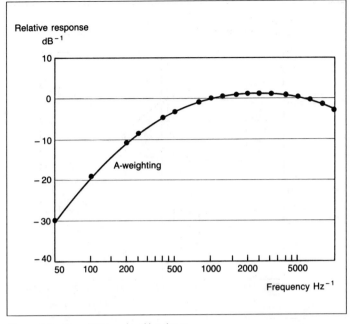

Figure 3.8   The dB(A) scale of loudness

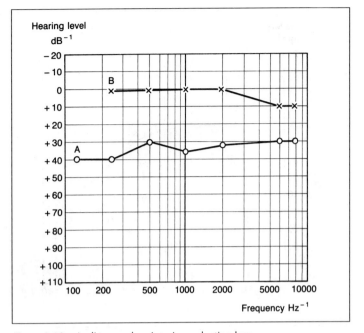

Figure 3.10   Audiogram showing air conduction loss

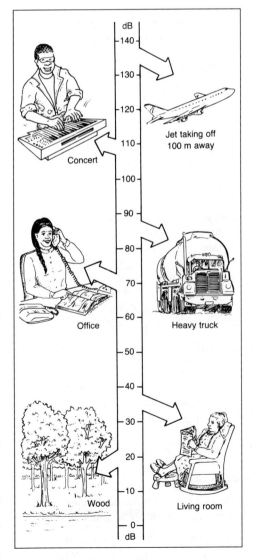

Figure 3.9   Everyday sound levels in dB

The weighting factors used in the dB(A) scale produce a set of curves similar to Figure 3.8.

Typical sound levels in dB encountered in daily life are shown in Figure 3.9.

The minimum change in power which the ear is able to detect is about 1 dB, which corresponds to an increase in power of 25%. At low intensities the ear can distinguish smaller changes in intensity than is possible at high intensities.

If the lowest intensity required for the detection of a sound is plotted for different frequencies, the plot – known as an **audiogram** – is said to show the **threshold of audibility**.

Audiometry

Hearing threshold levels are determined by means of a device known as an **audiometer**. The audiometer produces sounds by means of an electrical circuit which produces pure frequency oscillations in an electromagnet, coupled to either an earphone or an electronic vibrator. The earphone is used to test the air conduction of the sound, while the electronic vibrator tests the bone conduction of the sound and is placed on the mastoid bone.

The controls within the audiometer allow the operator to control both the frequency and amplitude of the oscillations.

The audiometer is calibrated so that the zero intensity level measured in dB at each frequency is the mean loudness that can just be heard for a group of 'normal' people. If the loudness of a tone must be increased by 30 dB for a particular patient, then that patient is said to have a hearing loss of 30 dB at that frequency.

In a standard audiometric examination, the operator tests the patient over a range of 8 frequencies from 125 Hz to 8 kHz. At each frequency the intensity level (in dB) at which the patient can just hear the sound is determined. A plot of the patient's sensitivity to the sounds against their frequency – an **audiogram** – can then be made.

Figure 3.10 shows an audiogram for a patient who has normal bone conduction thresholds (B) but a 40 dB loss for air conduction (A).

Defects of hearing

There are two types of deafness. The first, called **nerve deafness** (or **sensory neural loss**), occurs when the cochlear nerve, the auditory nerve or the brain is damaged. The second, known as **conduction deafness**, occurs when the conduction mechanisms in the inner ear are impaired.

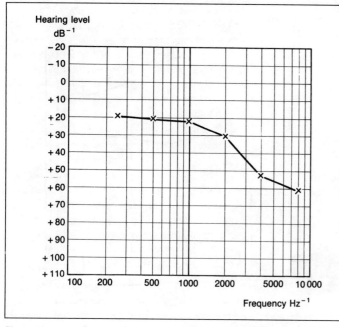

Figure 3.11 Audiogram showing reduced high-frequency hearing

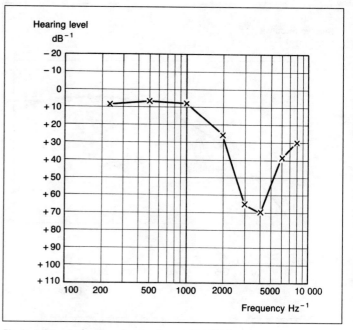

Figure 3.12 Audiogram showing loss at specific frequency

Sensory neural loss

There are many causes of this defect. Congenital cochlear deafness can be caused in children by the rubella virus in the mother whilst pregnant. A viral infection can damage the cochlear nerve. Tumours can damage the nerve cells or the brain stem. Damage occuring as a result of long-term exposure to high intensities of sound is also sensory neural damage.

Until recently, damage of either the cochlear nerve or the auditory nerve meant permanent deafness. Recently a new technique of cochlear implantation has been developed. In this operation electrodes are implanted within the cochlear. Sound is then converted to an electrical signal which is passed via the electrodes to the nerve endings within the cochlear. The conversion is such that different frequencies of sound cause different electrodes to be activated. For the technique to be effective, the patient must have had hearing at one time, but even so has to re-learn 'how to hear'.

Tinnitus is another neural hearing defect. The cause of this disease is not understood, but the effect is to hear a ringing sound all the time at one or more frequencies. It is as though the nerve is constantly being stimulated in the absence of any sound. Partial relief can be effected by masking the 'sound'.

To do this a small electrical current is passed into the ear via the mastoid protrusion for a period of an hour or more. The frequency of the stimulus is varied around the frequency of the ringing. The theory is that the brain is overstimulated by the stimulus, and the sensitivity to that frequency is reduced for a short period. Developing effective methods of relieving tinnitus are necesary because

its psychological effects are so great in some cases that sufferers may be driven to suicide.

Conduction hearing loss

If any of the conduction mechanisms of the middle ear are damaged there will be a loss of hearing. To distinguish this form of hearing loss from that of neural hearing loss, the hearing via bone conduction is tested at the same time as air conduction. A malfunction of the middle ear is indicated if there is normal bone conduction with reduced air conduction.

There are many causes of conductive hearing loss – for example, wax in the ear canal, damage to the tympanic membrane, or damage to the ossicles either by trauma or disease. Respiratory infections can result in the build-up of fluid in the middle ear which will also interfere with the passage of sound. This is a relatively common problem in children, and is often referred to as 'glue ear'.

Age-related deafness

Figure 3.11 shows the audiogram for an elderly person whose threshold of hearing at all the higher frequencies is reduced both for bone and air conduction. This happens because the base of the basilar membrane, where high frequencies are detected, has become damaged with age.

Noise-induced deafness

Long-term exposure to high intensity noise levels (90 dB or more) may result in deafness.

Noise-induced deafness is usually characterised at first by a dip in the sensitivity of the hearing at around 4 kHz (Figure 3.12). In the later stages of

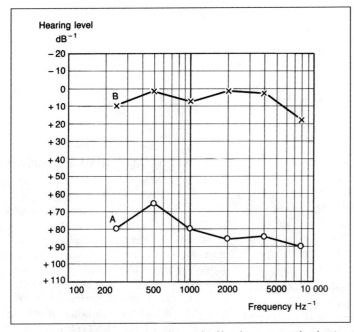

Figure 3.13   Audiogram showing the result of brief exposure to loud noise

the condition all frequencies become affected. The effect is usually only permanent if the exposure is for five years or more.

The people most likely to be affected are sheet metal workers, riveters, mill workers and those who work in the staging of pop concerts. Those who visit pop concerts on an occasional basis may suffer a temporary hearing reduction but will not become permanently deaf. Long-term use of personal stereos may possibly induce later permanent deafness, as with the case of high levels of industrial noise, but this has not yet been proved.

Brief exposure to loud noises can result in major changes to the audiogram. One such example is shown in Figure 3.13.

Questions

1. a) i)   A sound level meter measuring the noise from a tractor in the open air gave a reading of 76 dB. The tractor was then driven into a large hall for an agricultural exhibition and the meter reading rose to 94 dB. Calculate the ratio of the intensity of sound inside the hall to that outside.

   ii)   Explain why the meter used for the measurements should be scaled in dBA.

   b) i)   Sketch a graph showing the threshold of hearing for a young person with good hearing as a function of frequency, marking approximate scales on the axes. Using the same axes, sketch a graph of the threshold for the same person after being exposed for more than a year to noise levels such as those from the tractor indoors without wearing ear defenders.

   ii)   State how the deterioration of hearing with age differs from that due to exposure to excessive noise.

2. a)   With the aid of a labelled diagram of the middle ear, explain how sound energy is transmitted across the tympanic cavity. Give a reason why the pressure changes due to sound are increased as a result of this transmission and state an approximate value for the increase.

   b)   A meter, which measures relative intensity level of sound referred to 1 pW m^{-2}, records a value of 97 dB when a pneumatic drill is switched on some distance away.

   Calculate the intensity level of sound at the meter.

   A second drill, identical to the first, is placed close to it. State the intensity of sound at the meter when both drills are working, and hence calculate the *increase* in the meter reading.

   Explain why it is convenient to use the decibel scale for such measurements.

3. a)   Explain what is meant by the **intensity of sound** and indicate how the loudness perceived is related to the intensity received at the ear.

   Calculate the intensity of the loudest sound the ear can withstand given that the intensity level, referred to a threshold for human hearing of 10^{-12} W m^{-2}, of the same sound is 120 dB.

   b)   The eye has a threshold for perception when 100 photons per second of wavelength 510 nm enter the pupil. The effective area of the external entrance of the auditory canal (auditory meatus) is 65 mm^2.

   If the threshold sensitivity of either organ is defined as the least power required to produce a perceptible signal, calculate the ratio of the threshold sensitivity of the eye to that of the ear.

   Comment on the significance you think this result has for man.

   Planck's constant $= 6.6 \times 10^{-34}$ J s
   Speed of light $= 3.0 \times 10^{8}$ m s^{-1}

4   ELECTRICAL CONDUCTION

The organisation of the nervous system

The functions of the body are controlled by the nervous system which is made up of the brain, spinal cord, nerves and muscles. The nerves consist of bundles of nerve cells or neurones – specialised cells down which electrical pulses pass.

There are two different kind of neurones, sensory and motor neurones. The ends of sensory neurones are sensitive to temperature, light or pressure. A change in one of these properties will trigger or activate an electrical impulse in the neurone. If, for instance, a temperature-sensitive neurone undergoes a change in temperature, it generates an electrical impulse which travels up the nerve fibre to the brain. Motor neurones carry electrical impulses from the brain to the muscles or organs in order to make them move or otherwise alter their activity. The brain determines which motor neurones will be stimulated.

The nervous system is like a computer (the brain) which is connected by wires (the nerve fibres) to detectors (the ends of sensory nerves). It is programmed to send signals (via the motor nerves) to machines capable of doing work (the muscles) if the value of the property being detected goes outside certain limits.

The following simple example will illustrate how the system works. If a match is held to the hand, a temperature-sensitive nerve will be stimulated because the temperature is outside the range normally expected. This nerve will send an electrical signal to the brain or spinal cord. The brain will interpret this as 'ouch, my hand is hot', and send a signal to the muscles of the hand instructing them to pull the hand away.

Of course, the whole sequence of events takes place in a much shorter time that it takes to describe it. It takes perhaps less than a second, giving some indication as to how quickly the impulses travel to and from the brain down the neurones.

Within the brain and spinal cord there exists a complicated network of neurones connecting the sensory and motor neurones. These connections act as gates controlling the direction of the signals.

The electrical action of the nerves and muscles is related to the biochemistry of the cell, as will be described in more detail in this chapter.

The structure and function of the nerves

The neurones consist of a main body with hair-like dendrites which radiate from it, and a long thin extension (the nerve fibre) which is few micrometers in diameter but may be up to a metre long. The nerve fibres of myelinated nerves are covered by an insulating layer of myelin which has many breaks (nodes of Ranvier) in it. These nerves conduct electricity much faster than unmyelinated cells. Figure 4.1 shows a typical motor neurone.

A neurone can be thought of as a long cylinder made up of a cell membrane. There are fluids both inside the cell and outside it. These fluids contain many ions, the most important being potassium, sodium and calcium ions. Normally ions diffuse throughout a solution until they are evenly distributed, and negative and positive charges are as far as possible evenly matched.

If at any time there is a greater concentration of positive ions in one part than another, then an electrical potential will exist between areas of high concentration and areas of low concentration. This electrical potential will exert a force on the ions, making them tend to move from the higher to the lower concentration, rather as water flows downhill. Taking the water analogy further, there

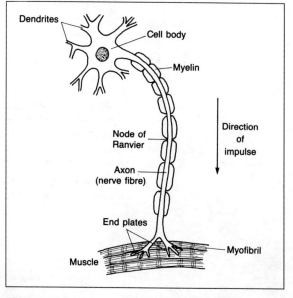

Figure 4.1   A motor neurone showing myelinated nerve fibre and cell body

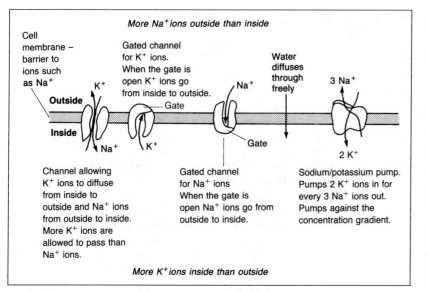

Figure 4.2   The cell membrane, the fluids on either side and the channels through the membrane

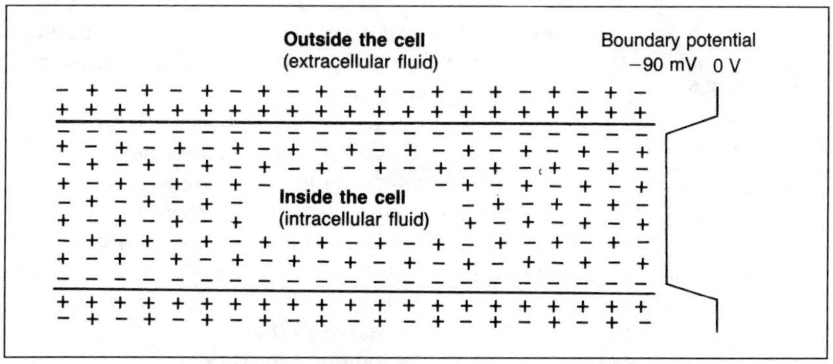

Figure 4.3   The distribution of ions in the intracellular and extracellular fluids for a nerve fibre in the resting state

potassium ions from outside to inside. These pumps move ions from the side of the membrane with the lower concentration to that with the higher (like pumping water uphill), since there is a higher concentration of sodium ions outside the cell and a higher concentration of potassium ions inside.

The concentrations of the positive sodium, potassium and calcium ions in the fluids very close to the neurone membrane are usually different either side. Elsewhere in the fluids there are almost equal numbers of positive ions and negative ions. If a probe measuring electrical potential were inserted in the fluids outside or inside the cell at any point except very close to or across the cell membrane, there would be no electrical potential recorded.

Figure 4.3 shows the situation where a minute excess of positive ions is found outside the neurone, distributed along the membrane. A small excess of negative ions is found inside the cell, also ranged along the membrane. The negative ions in the electrolytic solutions, for example chloride ions, do not play a major role in electrical conduction.

The net effect of this arrangement of positive and negative ions along the cell membrane is to make it act as a capacitor, which means that there is a potential difference across the cell membrane. Since the 'plates' of the capacitor are close together, the potential across the membrane can be quite large, even though the number of ions is quite small.

Resting potential

As we have seen, in the resting state there is a greater concentration of sodium ions outside the cell and of potassium ions inside. This imbalance is maintained by the sodium/potassium pump and results in a potential difference across the cell membrane.

The electric potential for a positive ion is calculated from the formula:

$$\text{e.m.f. in millivolts} = -61 \log_{10} \frac{\text{concentration on inside of cell}}{\text{concentration on outside of cell}}$$

This e.m.f. is known as the **Nernst potential**. For sodium ions it is +61 mV and for potassium ions −94 mV. If the ions were free diffuse we might expect a potential of −33 mV across the membrane as a result of these two potentials.

In fact, as described earlier, proteins in the membrane allow the small potassium ions to pass through quite freely and the large sodium ions less freely. In addition, the sodium/potassium pump pumps three potassium ions to the inside of the cell for every two sodium ions it pumps out.

The net effect of all this is that in the resting state the potassium ion gradient has more effect on the overall potential of the cell membrane than does the sodium ion gradient.

is said to be a **concentration gradient** (the hill) which encourages the ions to move from the higher to the lower concentration (downhill).

However, the ions in and around the cell are not allowed to move freely, as the cell membrane controls the movement of the ions close to it.

The cell membrane as shown in Figure 4.2 consists mainly of a bilipid layer which allows water molecules to pass through freely but prevents most water-soluble substances from passing through. This layer contains large protein molecules. Some of these proteins act as channels which allow particular ions such as sodium, potassium or calcium to leak slowly across the membrane in one direction. These channels are open all the time.

Other proteins act as a channel with a gate at one end. There are different gated channels for sodium and potassium ions. Ions can only pass through a gated channel if the gate is open. Normally the gates are closed, but they can be opened or activated by an electrical pulse.

In addition, some proteins act as pumps, pumping sodium ions from inside the cell to outside and

Diffusion and pumping occur until equilibrium is reached between the concentration gradient and the electric potential for a particular ion. The result is that a potential gradient of about –90 mV exists between the inside and the outside of the cell membrane. This is known as the **resting potential**. It can be seen that the value of the resting potential is close to that of the Nernst potential for the potassium ion. This shows that the potassium ion does indeed have more effect on the resting potential than does the sodium ion.

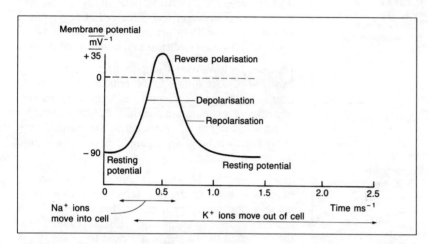

Figure 4.4   The action potential for a nerve cell

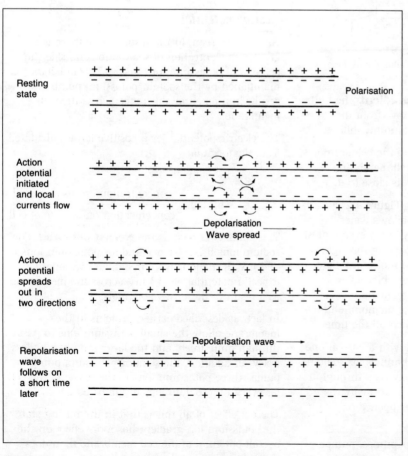

Figure 4.5   Propagation of an action potential along a conductive fibre

Action potential

Sensory neurones are activated by a change in the property they are sensitive to, while motor neurones are activated by an impulse from the brain or spinal cord.

As we have seen, certain proteins in the cell membrane allow sodium or potassium ions to pass through in one direction. These channels have gates which, when closed, stop the passage of the ions. In the resting state the channels are closed. When the neurone becomes activated the sodium gates open and allow sodium ions to rush into the cell. As stated previously, the electric potential across the cell membrane depends on the concentrations of the ions on either side. So this sudden change in the concentration of the sodium ions will alter the potential gradient.

Following the change in sodium concentration the potential gradient across the cell membrane goes through a series of very rapid changes. First the potential changes from –90 mV to 0 mV (**depolarisation**). It then overshoots and becomes positive (**reverse polarisation**). Within a fraction of a millisecond the membrane becomes impermeable to sodium ions because the change in concentration closes the sodium gates, but permeable to potassium ions because potassium gates are activated and so open. Potassium ions then move out of the cell and return the resting membrane potential to –90 mV again. In the resting state the concentrations of sodium and potassium ions are slowly restored to their original values by the action of the sodium/potassium pump.

The changes of membrane potential resulting from all this are shown in Figure 4.4. These rapid changes are known as **action potentials**.

Propagation of the nerve action potential

How does the impulse travel along the nerve fibre? The action potential described above occurs at one point on the neurone's membrane. However, the movement of the positive charges near this point on the membrane cause an increase in membrane potential for 1–3 nm on either side of the action point. This increase in membrane potential activates the sodium and potassium channels either side of the action point and causes depolarisation to occur there, thereby propagating the electrical impulse. The activation wave spreads out in two directions along the membrane, as shown in Figure 4.5.

Following behind the spread of the depolarisation wave comes the repolarisation wave.

The movement of ions during depolarisation and repolarisation gives rise to circulating currents and voltages outside the membrane. Figure 4.6 shows the potential gradient along a line P–P outside a membrane.

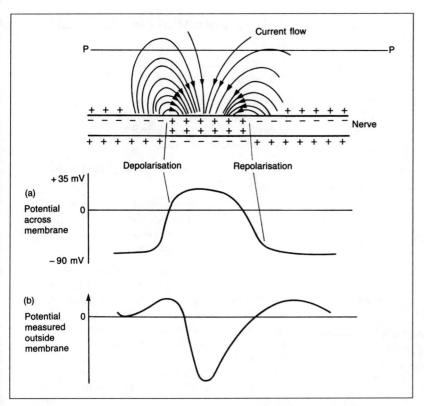

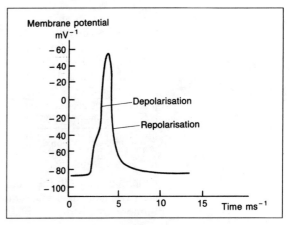

Figure 4.7   The muscle action potential

Figure 4.6
Depolarisation, current
flow and the electric
potential outside a
nerve

It should be pointed out that the action potentials
we have been considering take place along the
nerve fibres. These could be stimulated by placing
electrodes anywhere on the nerve fibre within the
body. Normally the nerve fibres are stimulated by a
generator potential emitted from the cell body
when a stimulus (light, heat, pressure or chemical)
is received by that body. In this way the impulse
takes a specific direction – in the case of sensory
cells towards the brain, and in the case of motor
cells away from the brain.

The duration of a neurone action potential is
0.2–1.0 ms, and the velocity of conduction is about
50–90 m s^{-1}. This means that the stimulus from a
neurone is received by the brain or spinal cord in a
fraction of a second and the neurone is then ready
to receive and conduct another impulse.

The speed and strength of a neurone impulse are
always the same – a stimulus can either cause an
action potential or not. The strength of a sensation
is determined by how many neurones within a
nerve bundle are stimulated, and by the frequency
(up to a maximum) of the transmitted pulses.

Excitation of skeletal muscle

Each motor neurone supplying a skeletal muscle
branches into many other smaller nerve fibres.
These nerve fibres are each attached by an **end-
plate junction** to a different muscle fibre. The
muscle fibres or myofibrils attached to one motor
neurone are termed one **motor unit** and may be
3–1000 in number.

When a stimulus reaches an end plate the end
plate releases a chemical which stimulates an
action potential in the myofibril to which it is
attached. The action potential is similar to that
described for a nerve action potential, except that it
is slower, as can be seen by comparing Figure 4.7
with Figure 4.4.

The resting membrane potential for a muscle fibre
is again ~–90 mV, but the action potential has a
duration of 1–5 ms, and a speed of conduction of
3–5 m s^{-1}. This means that the muscle action
potential lasts longer and is conducted less quickly
than the nerve action potential.

The flow of the action potentials within the muscle
fibres causes calcium ions to be released from
within the cells, and these calcium ions in turn
cause the muscle to contract for a period of
50–100 ms.

Each time an action potential passes along a
muscle fibre a small electric current spreads out
and may reach as far as the skin. Thus, if
electrodes are placed on the skin, or if needle
electrodes are inserted into the muscle, an electrical
recording or **electromyogram** (**EMG**) can be
made. Figure 4.8 shows the large spikes due to

Figure 4.8
EMG from needle
electrodes in
(a) weakly contracting
muscle (b) strongly
contracting muscle

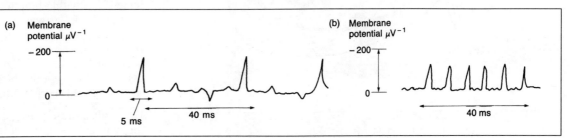

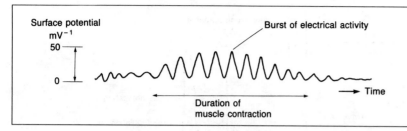

Figure 4.9   EMG from surface electrode when a single muscle is stimulated

action potentials in the motor unit near a needle electrode and small spikes due to action potentials in more distant motor units.

If surface electrodes are used, the sum of many action potentials in different directions is recorded. This looks more like random noise. However, if a single muscle is stimulated, a burst of activity will be recorded on the EMG. Figure 4.9 shows such a recording from a normal muscle.

Deviations from the normal EMG trace occur when the motor nerves to the muscle are damaged, either from the effects of a disease such as poliomyelitis, or from some trauma.

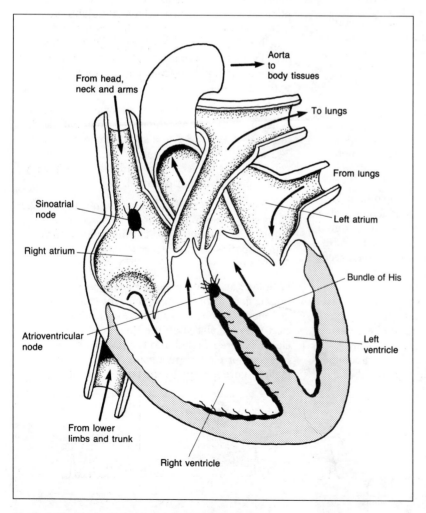

Figure 4.10   The heart and its conduction muscles

Action potentials in the heart muscle

The action of the heart

The heart is made up of a special kind of muscle, cardiac muscle. Before looking at the action potentials in the heart, it will be helpful to outline its mechanical action.

The heart acts as two mechanical pumps side by side, as shown in Figure 4.10.

Each pump consists of two chambers. The upper chambers of the heart are known as the atrial chambers and serve as priming pumps for the lower chambers or ventricles.

Deoxygenated blood from the tissues is pumped by the chambers on the right-hand side to the lungs where it is reoxygenated. The reoxygenated blood then enters the upper chamber on the left-hand side where it is pumped round the body to oxygenate the tissues. The blood then returns to the right-hand chambers and the process is repeated. The chambers of the heart are separated by valves so that the blood can only flow in one direction.

Attached to the right atrium is a small muscle, the **sinoatrial node** (SA node). A small bundle of fibres, the **atrioventricular bundle** (AV bundle) connects the atria and the ventricles.

Rhythmic excitation of the heart

Cardiac muscle is stimulated to contract by action potentials in a manner similar to that for skeletal muscle. However, cardiac muscle has a few extra properties.

Cardiac muscle has an extra channel in its cell membranes for transport of calcium ions. The effect of this channel on the action potential is to prolong the depolarisation phase, forming a plateau on the action potential curve. The resultant action potential is shown in Figure 4.11.

The plateau lasts 250 ms, during which time the cell is not sensitive to further stimuli. This means that the muscle cannot be restimulated to contract within this time, and allows full relaxation of the muscle before the next contraction.

All the muscles of the heart consist of self-excitory tissue – that is, the stimulation of the muscle cells comes from within and not from an external nerve from the brain, as was the case with skeletal muscle. Each cardiac muscle cell has a cycle whereby charges build up along its membrane, are discharged, and then build up again. Even if heart tissue is removed from the body, the cells will still go through this cycle until they die.

The cardiac muscle cells are so arranged that stimulation of any one of the heart muscle fibres

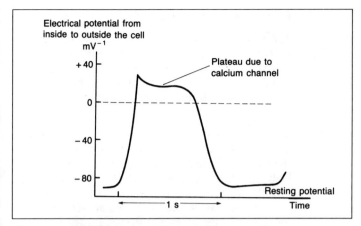

Figure 4.11   The action potential for a cardiac muscle fibre

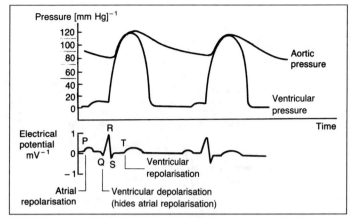

Figure 4.12   The pressure waveforms in the ventricles and aorta as a function of time, together with the corresponding electrical potential waveforms

causes the depolarisation wave to spread over the whole muscle mass in a very short space of time, causing the whole heart to contract.

However, the rhythm of the heart is ultimately controlled by the sinoatrial node (SA node) or the natural pacemaker, because this has the fastest rhythm. The SA node beats normally in the adult about 72 times per minute; in a baby about 90 times per minute.

The SA node initiates the depolarisation wave which sweeps across the atria causing them to contract, resulting in the P wave shown in Figure 4.12. The wave is stopped by non-conducting fibrous tissue which forms a boundary between the atria and the ventricles. The only path it can take is through the AV bundle, which conducts electricity slowly. After passing through the AV bundle the depolarisation wave is rapidly distributed across the ventricles causing them to contract. This wave corresponds in time to the QRS wave in Figure 4.12. Because the muscle masses

are separated in this way it is possible for the atria to contract a short time ahead of the ventricles.

The last part of the cycle is the repolarisation of the muscle cells, and the refilling of the atria and ventricles with blood, corresponding to the T wave in Figure 4.12. Each cycle corresponds to one heartbeat.

When the ventricles contract, blood is pushed out of them into the pulmonary artery and aorta. The periods of contraction are known as **systole** and the periods of relaxation **diastole**.

The pressure changes with time in the atria and ventricles are shown in Figure 4.12, together with the depolarisation curves.

The electrocardiogram

During each heartbeat, action potentials spread out from the atria to the ventricles. This causes differences in potential between adjacent tissues.

However, the heart is surrounded by tissues and fluids which conduct electricity well. Any changes in potentials of the heart muscle will therefore result in electric current flowing from depolarised areas to polarised areas in large circuitous routes, as shown in Figure 4.13.

The average current flow is from the base of the heart (where the atria are) to the apex (the pointed end formed by the ventricles) during most of the depolarisation cycle.

If two electrodes are placed on the chest, with the positive electrode nearer the apex of the heart than the negative, and connected to a voltmeter, a small positive voltage will be recorded as in Figure 4.13.

If the electrodes are connected to an oscilloscope or a pen recorder moving on a paper trace, the variation of the voltage with time can be displayed. Because the voltages are very small (of the order of one millivolt) they must be amplified before being displayed or recorded. Such a voltage display or

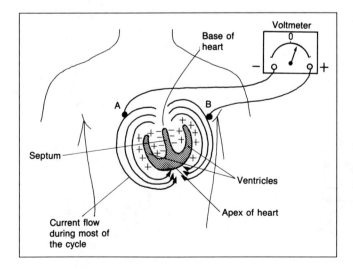

Figure 4.13   The currents flowing round the heart and voltage recorded during most of the heart's cycle between two electrodes placed on the chest

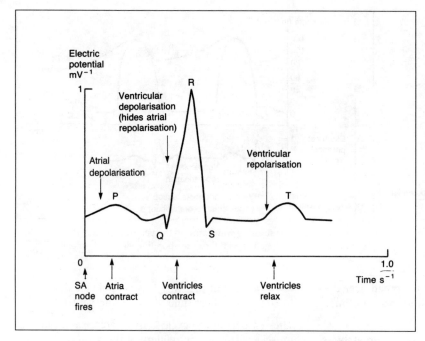

Figure 4.14
Typical ECG trace

Positioning of the electrodes

The exact shape and size of the voltages recorded in an ECG depend greatly on where the electrodes are placed. Usually three electrodes are placed at standard sites. The potential of one of the electrodes is compared with the average potential of the other two.

Each combination of electrodes is known as a **lead**. Below are the three bipolar limb leads which record the electrical potential between two points on the body. The leads must be attached to the meter through a large resistance so that little current is taken by the meter and the potentials are not disturbed by the measuring device. Figure 4.15 illustrates the positions of the leads.

Lead I   Right arm and left arm
Lead II   Right arm and left leg
Lead III   Left arm and left leg

In addition, the following leads are sometimes used to measure the difference in potential between one limb and the average of two other limbs.

aVR   Right arm and left arm and leg
aVL   Left arm and left leg and right arm
aVF   Left leg and right and left arm

If **arrythmias** of the heart – fluctuations in its normal steady rhythm – are to be recorded, the choice of site of the electrodes is not important, as

tracing is known as an **electrocardiogram** or **ECG**.

Figure 4.14 shows a typical ECG curve. At point P on the curve the atria depolarise, at QRS the ventricles depolarise, and at T ventricular repolarisation occurs. The atria repolarise while the ventricles depolarise (during the QRS peak), and do not provide a characteristic curve on the ECG.

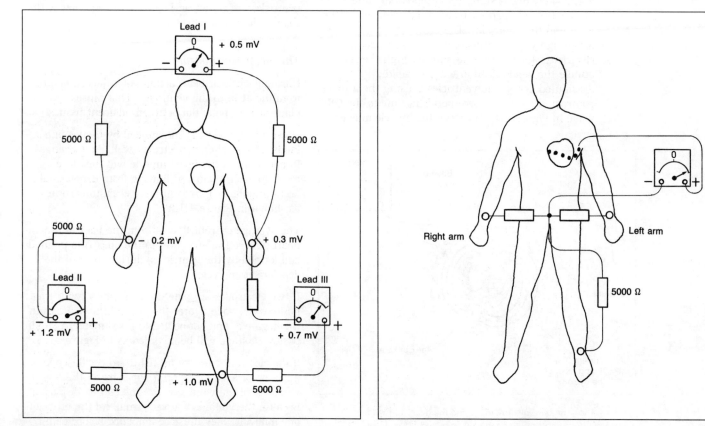

Figure 4.15   Conventional arrangement for bipolar limb leads

Figure 4.16   ECG with six chest leads and three limb leads

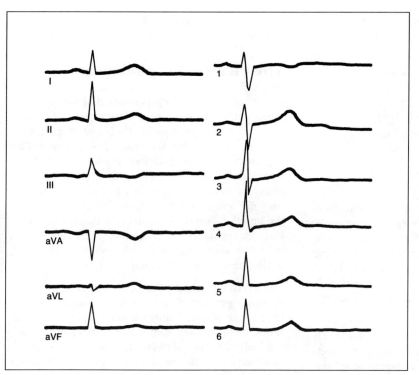

Figure 4.17
ECGs of one single
cycle measured at six
chest positions and six
bipolar limb positions

any of the possible arrangements of leads will provide the QRS complex. However, if damage to the muscle in particular areas of the heart is to be traced, then the position of the electrodes becomes much more important and the arrangement in Figure 4.16 is used, where the potential at one of six chest sites is compared with the average potential in the limbs.

One lead is placed at a choice of six sites over the heart, whilst the other three leads are connected via high resistances to both arms and the left leg. In practice all six chest sites are connected to the recording oscilloscope and are sampled separately. The recordings from each chest lead will reflect the electrical potential of the cardiac muscle just below it, and any abnormality in the recording will suggest a malfunction in that part of the heart.

Figure 4.17 shows the ECGs recorded during one cycle at the six chest leads used here and six bipolar limb leads.

Practical considerations

The electrical potentials recorded in the ECG are very small, of the order of 1 mV. It is therefore necessary to pass the signals through a high-gain amplifier before they are displayed on the oscilloscope or recorded on paper tape.

The frequency of the ECG cycle is usually less than 2 Hz. Movement of the patient may cause the electrodes to move on the skin surface, resulting in sharp spikes in the voltages generated. The sharp spikes have the same effect as a signal of high frequency. Any unwanted random voltage present on a desired signal is known as **noise**. These spikes are therefore said to introduce high-frequency noise

in the electrode signal. The high-frequency noise needs to be filtered out of the signal.

Nearby apparatus may also introduce 50 Hz noise into the system from the mains alternating current. Whenever a 50 Hz alternating current runs in a circuit, a changing electric field is generated which may induce small alternating voltages of 50 Hz in other circuits nearby. These unwanted e.m.f.s are known as '50 Hz noise' and cause many problems in the hospital environment. It is not always possible to screen off all surrounding apparatus, and in any case the leads from the mains may themselves cause the problem. It is therefore advisable to filter out the 50 Hz frequency.

One possibility would be to filter out all frequencies above 2 Hz, the normal frequency of the ECG, but this would distort the wave shape. If monitoring the heart rate is the only purpose of the ECG, then frequencies greater than 40 Hz can be filtered out. However, in diagnosis, the wave shape is more important, and this is only reproduced faithfully if frequencies up to 100 Hz are kept. In this case the apparatus should have careful shielding to reduce 50 Hz noise.

Disposable silver chloride-coated silver electrodes are used to connect the patient to the ECG monitor. These electrodes do not become polarised, that is ions do not build up near their surfaces and impede the current flow as happens with platinum electrodes, and they are not toxic as are copper electrodes.

The electrodes take the form of adhesive pads with a central cap containing a gel which conducts electricity well to ensure good electrical contact. Each pad has a strip of abrasive surface material used for rubbing away hairs and dead skin which have a high impedance. Usually a contact impedance of about 10 kΩ is achieved, which will ensure that the waveform is not distorted by most amplifiers which have an input impedance of about 1 MΩ.

The patient must be relaxed, as any anxiety will be reflected in the ECG. The heart will beat faster and more irregularly in the anxious state, and a true diagnosis will not be possible. In addition any muscular movement must be minimised to avoid noise on the ECG.

Of course, when connecting any electrical apparatus to a patient, the circuitry connected to the mains must be isolated from the patient. This is usually done by using transformer isolation or opto-isolation.

The use of ECG measurements

By studying the ECG of a patient, much can be deduced about the functioning or malfunctioning of the heart. ECGs are taken from patients in the operating theatre and intensive care units, and from patients thought to have suffered a heart attack.

In heart failure the QT interval is lengthened. Patients who are thought to have milder heart complaints are given carefully supervised exercise tests using a treadmill or exercise bike in order to record the functioning of the heart under increasing stress.

A reduced QRS pulse height indicates possible reduced ventricular contraction.

In elderly people there is sometimes a malfunction of the SA node causing either a very fast heart beat (**flutter**) or an irregular repetition rate (**fibrillation**) and irregular pumping. Under these circumstances artificial stimulation needs to be provided. This is done using a small, implanted electronic unit known as an artificial pacemaker.

Life-threatening fibrillation can also occur as a result of electric shock from weak a.c. current. This results in the smooth spread of the depolarisation wave being interrupted for long enough to set up irregular impulses around the ventricles.

Defibrillation

Fibrillation can be stopped by passing a very strong d.c. current through the ventricles for a short time. This is known as **defibrillation** and is accomplished by placing two electrodes (paddles) on either side of the heart and passing the current down them, Figure 4.18. This causes repolarisation in all areas of the muscle at the same time. The heart stops beating erratically, is still for a moment, and then upon receiving a signal down the SA node begins to beat normally again.

The short current pulse of about 50 A is produced by discharging a capacitor which is connected in series to an inductance, through the electrodes. The capacitor is of the order of 16 μF and charges to 7000 V. With these high currents and voltages it is

wise for personnel other than the operator to stand well back as the defibrillation current is passed!

The electroencephalogram

It has been mentioned previously that many sensory and motor neurones terminate in the brain, and that complicated pathways connecting these neurones exist within the brain. The direction of an impulse along these pathways is controlled firstly so that impulses travel from sensory neurones to motor neurones, and secondly so that the correct response follows on from the stimulus applied. As the impulses travel by means of action potentials through the neurones in the brain, electrical potentials spread out to the surface of the skull during periods of stimulation.

One nerve fibre discharging on its own would not generate a potential large enough to be detected at the surface of the skull but if many fibres discharge simultaneously their sum may be detectable at the skull surface. Thus if electrodes are placed on the outer surface of the head, then continuous changes in the electrical potential can be recorded. The recording made of these changes is known as an **electroencephalogram**, or **EEG**.

Silver chloride-coated silver electrodes are used to attach the EEG monitor to the scalp. The scalp must be abraded and alcohol applied before the electrode is put into place in order to make a good contact.

The 'brain waves' have amplitudes of approximately 0–300 μV, and frequencies of 1–50 Hz. Most of the time the waves have no regular pattern, but under certain conditions four distinct patterns can be found in 'normal' people:

(a) The alpha wave with frequencies of 8–13 Hz which is found in the quiet resting state

(b) The beta wave which has a frequncy of 14–100 Hz and occurs when a person is concentrating on some mental activity or is tense

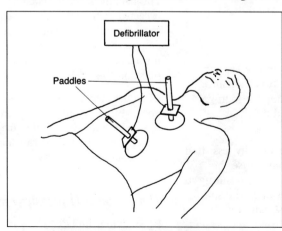

Figure 4.18   The defibrillator which gives several thousand volts for a few milliseconds to stop ventricular fibrillation

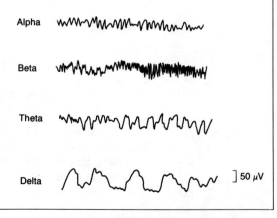

Figure 4.19   Four typical EEG waves

(c) The theta wave of 0.2–3.5 Hz which occurs in people experiencing emotional stress

(d) The delta wave with a frequency of 4–7 Hz which is found either in deep sleep or in the case of serious organic brain disease.

Typical examples of these four types of waves are shown in Figure 4.19.

EEGs are used in the diagnosis of epilepsy and brain tumours or other brain damage, when large amplitude slow waves are seen. They are also used in operating theatres to monitor the effects of anaesthesia.

Electroconvulsive shock therapy

Electroconvulsive shock therapy or **ECT** is used to treat some patients who have mental depression. In this so-called 'therapy' an electric shock is used to cause a generalised seizure similar to that of an epileptic attack. After the treatment the patient suffers memory loss for two to three weeks. There is no understanding as yet as to the method by which this occurs.

The method seems to have originated at a time when electricity was a new phenomenon, and was thought to have many curative properties. There seems no good reason why it is still used today and there are many doubts as to the virtue of treating such a delicate structure as the brain in this fashion.

Summary

1. Cells contain sodium and potassium ions. In the resting state there is a greater concentration of sodium ions outside the cell than inside. Conversely there is a greater concentration of potassium ions inside than outside.

2. An electrical pulse opens the sodium gates and allows sodium ions to flood into the cells. This gives rise to the changes in potential known as the action potential.

3. In turn the action potential gives rise to an electrical impulse travelling in a nerve.

4. In sensory nerves the impulse arises in the nerve end and travels to the brain. In motor nerves the pulse arises in the brain and travels to the muscles or other organs where it cause the muscles to contract. In the heart muscle many small impulses are repeatedly created within the muscle itself causing it to contract at regular intervals.

5. The electrical impulses give rise to small changes in electrical potential on the skin surface. These potentials can be used to follow the action of the heart, the muscles, or the brain, that is, ECG, EMG or EEG recordings respectively.

Questions

1. What do you understand by 'resting potential' and 'an action potential'? Show the voltage changes occuring during the course of an action potential giving approximate values.

2. Give the names of three kinds of recordings of electrical potential on the body surface caused by action potentials. Give examples of where they are used. What properties must an amplifier have in order to produce a voltage for display on an oscilloscope monitor?

3. Draw the shape of a typical ECG trace corresponding to one heartbeat. Mark on the relevent points at which there are changes in voltage. Explain how the trace is formed.

5 PHYSIOLOGICAL MEASUREMENTS

Measuring changes in physiological processes

Physiology is defined as the study of all the life processes, activities and functions of the body and its organs and tissues. Within the field of Medical Physics, physiological measurements involve measuring the changes in physical properties of different parts of the body. The most common physiological measurements to be made are those of temperature, force, pressure and flow.

Usually the most convenient way of measuring a physiological change is to convert the change in the property under study to a proportional change in some other physical property. One example is the thermometer which transforms changes in temperature to changes in the length of a column of liquid in a tube. In order to convert physiological changes into the physical changes that can be measured, **transducers** are used.

Transducers

Transducers transfer energy from one system to energy in another system. For example, physiological signals are often transformed by means of a transducer into an electrical voltage or current, whose amplitude varies with the

magnitude of the physiological signal. Figure 5.1 shows a schematic view of this system.

Transducers used with Wheatstone bridges

Very often, transducers are used in which the resistance of some component changes with the property being measured. The resistance of the component will be measured most accurately by placing it in one arm of a Wheatstone bridge and recording the voltage across the output terminals.

Figure 5.2 shows a varing resistance R_1 in one arm of a Wheatsone bridge.

Using the terminology of Figure 5.2, the output V_{out} of the bridge is given by:

$$V_{out} = \frac{R_1}{R_1 + R_4} V_{in} - \frac{R_2}{R_2 + R_3} V_{in}$$

If all the resistors are initially equal to R but R_1 changes by δR:

$$V_{out} = \frac{R(1 + \delta R/R)}{R(1 + \delta R/R) + R} V_{in} - \frac{R}{R + R} V_{in}$$

$$= \frac{2 + 2\delta R/R - 2 - \delta R/R}{2(2 + \delta R/R)} V_{in}$$

$$= V_{in} \frac{\delta R/R}{4(1 + \delta R/2R)}$$

If $\delta R/R \ll 1$:

$$V_{out} = \frac{V_{in}}{4} \delta R/R$$

This means the output voltage is proportional to the change in resistance. If the change in resistance is made proportional to some physiological change, the the output will be proportional to that fractional change.

Often the changes in resistance are very small and to increase the effect, resistances which are affected by the physiological change are used in all four arms of the bridge, as shown in Figure 5.3. The resistors are placed so that two increase their resistance by δR with the change and two decrease their resistance by the same amount δR.

It can be shown using Kirchoff's laws that the output V_{out} is given by:

$$V_{out} = \frac{R_1}{R_1 + R_4} V_{in} - \frac{R_2}{R_2 + R_3} V_{in}$$

If all the resistors are initially of value R there will be zero output voltage.

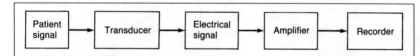

Figure 5.1   Stages in physiological measurement

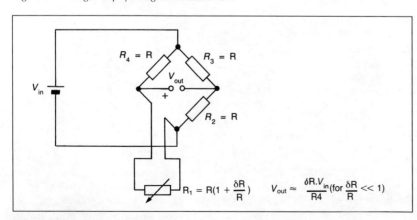

Figure 5.2   Resistance transducer in one arm of a Wheatstone bridge

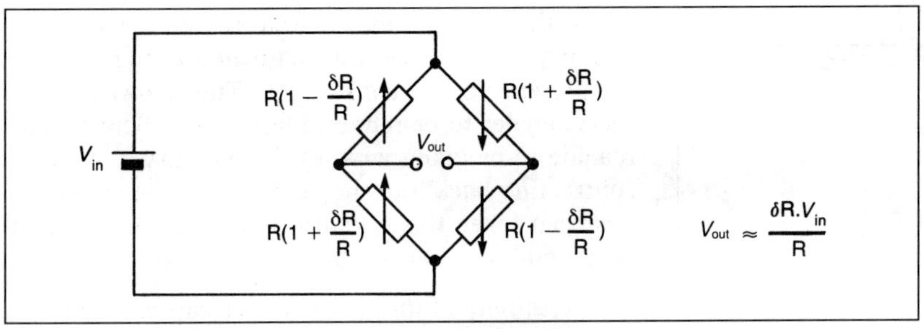

Figure 5.3   Resistance transducers in four arms of a Wheatstone bridge

If a change in pressure causes R_1 and R_3 to change to $R(1 + \delta R/R)$ whilst R_2 and R_4 change to $R(1 - \delta R/R)$ then:

$$V_{out} = \frac{R(1 + \delta R/R)}{R(1 + \delta R/R) + R(1 - \delta R/R)} V_{in} - \frac{R(1 - \delta R/R)}{R(1 - \delta R/R) + R(1 + \delta R/R)} V_{in}$$

$$V_{out} = \frac{R(1 + \delta R/R)}{2R} V_{in} - \frac{R(1 - \delta R/R)}{2R} V_{in}$$

$$= \delta R/R \; V_{in}$$

The change in the output voltage is four times as much as the change recorded if only one arm of the bridge is used as shown earlier.

If, however, there is a change in temperature, all the resistances will change by an equal amount in the *same direction*, that is either all positive or all negative, resulting in no change in the output voltage.

Amplifiers

The output current or voltage signals from transducers used in the field of medicine are usually very small – of the order of milliamps or millivolts. In most cases they need to be amplified and processed in other ways before being fed to some kind of recording device.

Recording devices

The recording device used with the transducer may be a paper trace, an oscilloscope or a computer. If a computer is used an extra device known as an analogue-to-digital converter (ADC) may be needed. The ADC samples the amplified voltage waveform at intervals in time and outputs the result in digital form to a computer.

Temperature measurements

The temperatures which are of most importance in the physiological system are the core temperature and the peripheral or skin temperature.

Core temperature

The organs of the body such as the brain, heart, digestive system and lungs, which are all deep body tissues, only operate efficiently within a narrow temperature range. The temperature of the deep body tissues is referred to as the **core temperature**.

A complicated temperature control mechanism exists within the body. This mechanism is under the control of an organ called the hypothalamus which works to ensure that the core temperature is kept constant to within +0.5 °C for ambient temperatures between 15 °C and 55 °C for the unclothed body. The actual core temperature varies between individuals but is usually in the range 36.2–37.3 °C.

Heat is produced within the body as a by-product of metabolism and is largely retained by the insulating layer of fat and skin. Heat can, however, be lost by conduction, convection, radiation and evaporation (sweating).

The body lowers its temperature by reducing metabolism and by increasing the blood flow to the skin blood vessels. It raises its temperature by shivering, increasing metabolism and reducing the blood flow to the skin blood vessels. The ambient temperatures at which blood flow is changed or sweating or shivering takes place depend greatly on whether the body is being exercised and on the rate of metabolism. Someone who is lying uncovered on a bed, neither moving nor eating, may well start shivering at temperatures which would cause a clothed healthy person to sweat (say 20 °C). This is the reason for keeping patients warm and well covered in hospitals.

The hypothalamus acts as a thermostat. It is connected to temperature sensors in the body. When it detects that the body is too cold or too hot it triggers the appropriate temperature-increasing or -decreasing mechanisms. In essence it acts as a feedback control on the body temperature.

The core temperature is usually measured in the mouth (orally) or the rectum (rectally). The temperature is considered normal if it is between 35.6 °C and 36.7 °C when measured orally, and 0.6 °C higher when measured rectally.

If the temperature control mechanism fails, for example during a feverish illness or after an operation, the temperature will be outside the normal range. Medical staff attach much importance to the measurement of core temperature in patients, using it as an indicator of their well-being.

For newborn babies who cannot yet regulate their temperature, incubators are used to maintain a constant temperature between 30 °C and 36 °C.

Skin temperature

The skin forms an insulating layer, keeping in the heat which is generated during metabolism and exercise. The temperature of the skin is dependent on the ambient temperature and varies normally

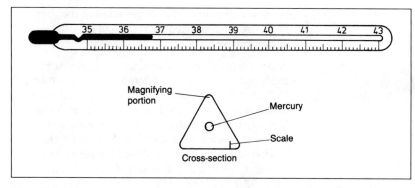

Figure 5.4   Mercury-in-glass thermometer

between 20 °C at very cold temperatures and 40 °C at very high temperatures.

Measurement of skin temperature can give an indication of the functioning of the temperature control systems within the body.

Temperature transducers

Methods of measuring temperature are many and varied, with mercury-in-glass thermometers, thermocouples, thermistors and semiconductors all being used. At the present time the methods most commonly used in medicine are the mercury-in-glass thermometer and the thermistor. Thermocouples may still be used in some cases but are largely being replaced by thermistors.

The choice of thermometer is dictated by the site in the body, the range required, and the speed of response and sensitivity needed by the device. For example, measurement of the temperatures of small internal organs or blood vessels requires the use of small devices with a fast response time.

The core temperature is most accurately measured at a depth of 8 cm within the body, which is difficult to achieve. The best approximation to this is given by a rectal thermometer, which is usually a thermistor. However, a reasonable estimate of the core temperature can be made more simply by using a mercury-in-glass thermometer placed in the mouth or under the armpit for a period of several minutes before taking a reading.

The mercury-in-glass clinical thermometer

The clinical thermometer, Figure 5.4, is made from a narrow-bore glass tube connected to a glass bulb containing mercury. The fine capillary has a constriction a short distance from the bulb.

When the bulb is heated, the mercury expands at a greater rate than the glass bulb and is pushed past the constriction, forming a silvery opaque column made more visible by means of the shape of the stem, which acts as a magnifying glass.

The distance that the mercury moves up the capillary is a measure of the change in temperature. Behind the tube is a scale marked out in tenths of a degree, against which the temperature can be read.

When the bulb is removed from the heat, the mercury is prevented from returning to the bulb by the presence of the constriction. This allows the thermometer to be removed from the patient and a reading to be taken without the mercury contracting back into the bulb. When the reading has been taken the mercury thread can be returned to the bulb by sharply shaking the thermometer.

The sensitivity of the thermometer can be increased by using a large bulb and a smaller bore tube, as this means that the mercury expands a greater distance up the tube for a smaller rise in temperature. However, the increase in thermal capacity of the bulb and the poor thermal contact with the patient means that the thermometer has a slow response time and is not very accurate. It is more difficult to read than the digital displays normally used for most modern instruments. Reasons of habit and cost, however, mean that it is still widely used.

Thermistors

Thermistors, or thermally sensitive resistors, are semiconductors with a resistance which varies inversely with the temperature. The rate of change of resistance with temperature is large for these semiconductors, typically 4.5% per °C at 25 °C.

Thermistors can be made in the form of beads (Figure 5.5(a)) about 0.5 mm in diameter and 0.2 mm thick. When the temperature changes there is a time lag before the resistance of the thermistor reaches its new value; this time lag is known as the **response time**. For a typical thermistor bead the response time is only a few seconds. This is because the bead is very small and soon reaches thermal equilibrium with the surrounding medium. A quick response time is important when a patient's temperature is changing rapidly, perhaps during and after major surgery.

The bead may be made of nickel, cobalt or manganese oxide mounted in glass. It is mounted on the end of a long cable which can be taped to the skin surface for skin temperature measurement or mounted in the tip of a catheter for insertion in the rectum, respiratory tract, oesophagus or bloodstream.

The variation of a thermistor's resistance with temperature is not simply inversely proportional, which would be a linear scale, but is very reproducible. It is usually varies as the negative exponential of the temperature

$$R = a.e^{-bt}$$

where R is the resistance, t the temperature, and a and b are constants. Figure 5.5(b) shows a typical thermistor characteristic.

In order to make the output of these devices directly proportional to the temperature,

Wheatstone bridge networks such as the one shown in Figure 5.5(c) are used.

The network in Figure 5.5(c) uses two thermistors made of different substances such that when used in the bridge circuit the net voltage output is directly proportional to the temperature, as shown in Figure 5.5(d).

The accuracy of these devices can be as high as ±0.1 °C in the range 0–60 °C.

The output of the bridge will usually be fed to either a calibrated galvanometer with a digital readout, or an oscilloscope if continuous monitoring of the temperature is needed.

Thermocouples

Thermocouples are used as an alternative to thermistors in temperature measurement. The principle of a thermocouple is that when two dissimilar metals are in contact, a potential

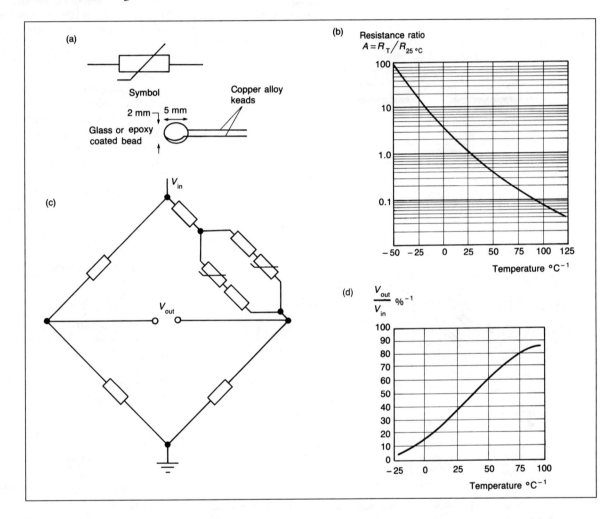

Figure 5.5
(a) Thermistor
(b) Typical thermistor characteristic (essentially logarithmic)
(c) Linearised thermistor circuit. V_{out} is proportional to T over a limited temperature range.
(d) Linearised thermistor output, linear over 5–65 °C

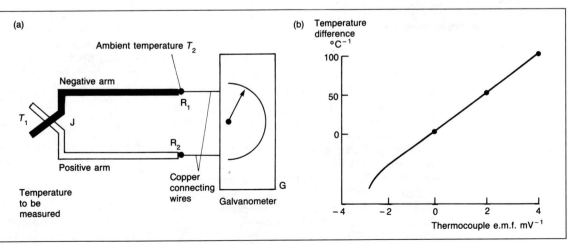

Figure 5.6
(a) Simple thermo-couple measuring temperature relative to ambient temperature
(b) Thermocouple output

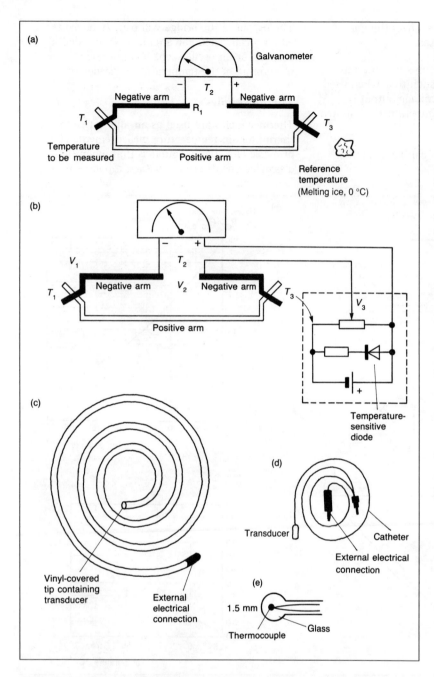

Figure 5.7   (a) Thermocouple measuring temperature relative to reference temperature
(b) Electronic circuitry to supply correction factor, $V_3 = f(T_3)$, for change in ambient
temperature   (c) General-purpose temperature probe   (d) Oesophogeal temperature
probe   (e) Miniature thermocouple bead

Figure 5.6(a) shows a simple thermocouple consisting of two wires, one of copper and the other of iron, soldered together at the junction J and connected to a galvanometer G. The wires are contained in a protective sheath. If the junctions J is heated and the rest of the circuit is at room temperature, electrons flow causing a current to be recorded on the galvanometer as shown in Figure 5.6(b). In practice such a simple device cannot be used. The connections to the galvanometer which are usually made of copper may themselves set up thermal e.m.f.s at the junctions R_1 and R_2 and the room temperature may vary.

The total potential generated will be a function of the difference in temperature between the junction J and the junctions at R_1 and R_2. To make the temperature measurement the junctions at R_1 and R_2 must be kept at a reference temperature. This could be 0 °C if the junctions were kept in flasks of crushed melting ice. This is not a practical solution in the medical situation.

More usually a circuit such as that shown in Figure 5.7(a) is used, where the net output depends on the difference between the temperature to be measured T_1 and the reference temperature T_3. But again a reference temperature T_3 is needed, and using crushed ice is not convenient. To avoid this, a circuit is used to compensate for variations in temperature (Figure 5.7(b)). The circuit generates a voltage which corresponds to that which would have been generated if the junctions were at 0 °C, by placing a temperature-sensitive transistor in the circuit.

The output from a typical thermocouple is 40 μV °C^{-1}. Once again the thermocouple is used as part of a bridge network coupled to an amplifier. Figures 5.7(c) and (d) show some practical thermocouple devices, and Figure 5.7(e) shows a thermocouple mounted in a glass bead.

Thermocouple devices can be calibrated very accurately, to within 0.01 °C, which is more than required for body temperatures. In addition, they are fairly robust. They used to have fairly slow response times, but can now be made with response times of 1 s. Their chief disadvantages are that they need a reference junction or a circuit which mimics one, and the amplifier systems used with the output from thermocouples need to be very carefully designed so that they do not affect the temperature when the circuit has been switched on for some time, and so that there very little 'noise'. Both these design problems make the amplifier systems very expensive.

The output voltage from the probe is fed to a suitably calibrated digital display or to a monitor continuously displaying the output.

difference exists between the metals as a result of the diffusion of electrons across their junction. For a particular pair of metals the junction potential is always the same at a particular temperature but is proportional (over a narrow range) to the temperature. If two metals are joined at two junctions forming an electrical circuit and a temperature difference exists between the two junctions, a current will flow. The current that flows will be proportional to the temperature difference between the two junctions.

Pressure measurements

Manometry

In medicine the main pressure measurements made are blood pressure, intracranial pressure, bladder pressure, respiratory pressure and pressure in the gastrointestinal tract. Occasionally pressures in the uterus and spinal fluid are also measured. These are all measurements of the pressure in fluids, or **manometry**.

The SI unit of pressure is the pascal (Pa), which is one newton per square metre (N m^{-2}). However, sometimes the millibar is used, where:

$$1 \text{ millibar} = 100 \text{ Pa}$$

Since the first pressure measurements to be made were blood pressure measurements, and these were made using columns of mercury, pressure is often measured in terms of millimetres of mercury (mm Hg), where:

$$1 \text{ millibar} = 100 \text{ Pa} = 0.75 \text{ mm Hg}$$

Some pressure measurements are made in millimetres of water (mm H$_2$O), and:

$$1 \text{ millibar} = 100 \text{ Pa} = 0.75 \text{ mm Hg}$$
$$= 10.2 \text{ mm H}_2\text{O}$$

Pressure transducers are used to convert the small pressure changes in the body into a variable voltage. The voltage can then be amplified, displayed on an oscilloscope screen, traced on a moving paper tape, or sampled by an ADC and recorded in computer memory or on computer disc.

Pressure transducers

Pressure is force per unit area, so if the area is constant only the force need be measured to determine the pressure. Most pressure transducers apply pressure to a diaphragm of uniform area. For this reason most pressure transducers are in fact based on strain gauges which measure force.

The resistance strain gauge

When a force is applied to a fine resistance wire, its length changes. Since the resistance R of a wire is given by:

$$R = \frac{\rho l}{A}$$

where l is the length of the resistor, A is the cross-sectional area, and ρ is the resistivity of the material of the resistor, any change in length will cause the resistance of the wire to change. See Figure 5.8(a).

Bonded and unbonded strain gauges

Unbonded strain gauges

Strain gauges can be wires or strips attached at one end to the surface being moved and at the other to a rigid support (Figure 5.8(b)). These are known as unbonded gauges. The resistance change in the strain gauge is proportional to the displacement of the surface.

Unbonded gauges are often used in sets of four, two being attached to each side of a diaphragm as shown in Figure 5.8(c). As the diaphragm is displaced by a positive pressure, two of the strain gauges will be extended and two compressed. If the pressure is reduced the two that were stretched are now compressed and vice versa. The reason for using four gauges is explained in the section on bonded strain gauges below.

Bonded strain gauges

Bonded strain gauges are made of long thin resistors bonded to a stiff base (see Figure 5.8(d)) or to a rubber membrane. The resistors can be made of wires, thin metal films or silicon with impurities in. Silicon resistors have 30 times the sensitivity of metal resistors.

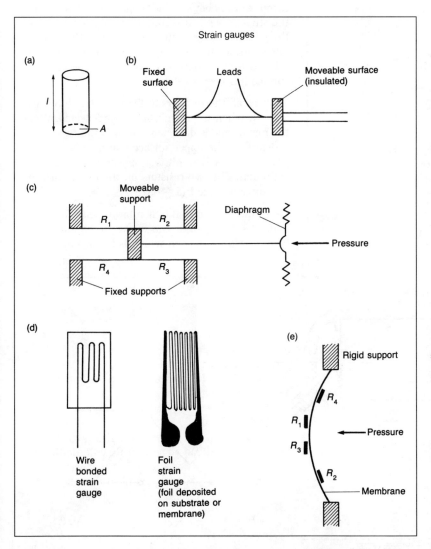

Figure 5.8 (a) $R = \rho l/A$ (b) Unbonded strain gauge (c) Four unbonded strain gauges used together (d) Practical bonded strain gauges (e) Four bonded strain gauges used together

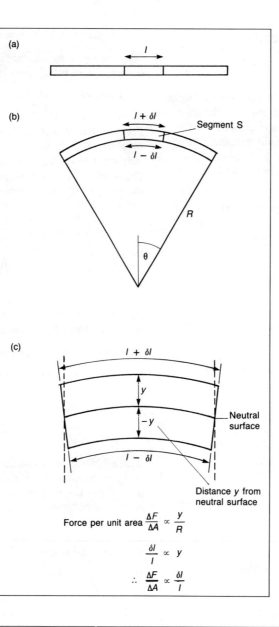

Figure 5.9
(a) Unbent rod or membrane
(b) Bent rod with radius of curvature R
(c) Longitudinal section of segment S

Force per unit area $\dfrac{\Delta F}{\Delta A} \propto \dfrac{y}{R}$

$$\dfrac{\delta l}{l} \propto y$$

$$\therefore \ \dfrac{\Delta F}{\Delta A} \propto \dfrac{\delta l}{l}$$

Figure 5.8(e) shows a typical arrangement for using bonded strain gauges in pressure measurements. Two of the gauges (R_1 and R_3) are placed on the top surface of the membrane and two (R_2 and R_4) on the lower surface of the membrane. As the membrane is deformed by the action of the increased differential pressure the two resistors R_1 and R_3 are stretched, and the two resistors R_2 and R_4, on the lower surface, are contracted. The reason for this is explained below.

Figure 5.9(b) shows the rod (or membrane) of Figure 5.9(a) being bent with a small curvature of radius R. Figure 5.9(c) shows a section of an enlarged segment of the same rod. The unbent length of the segment is l. Upon bending the upper surface at distance y from the mid-surface is stretched to become $l + \delta l$ and the lower surface at distance $-y$ from the mid-surface is contracted to become $l - \delta l$. The central surface stays the same length.

The full theory of the bending of rods and membranes is beyond the scope of this book, but if the student bends a rectangular rubber which has the midline marked out it will be seen that the lower surface has a shorter length than the midline – it has been compressed. Conversely the upper surface has been stretched.

Suppose all the resistors in Figure 5.8(e) have a value R when the membrane is undeflected. When the membrane is deflected upwards the two resistors on the upper surface will have a value of $R(1 + \delta R/R)$ where δR is proportional to the deflection. The two resistors on the lower surface will have a value $R(1 - \delta R/R)$.

As an alternative to the membrane with four bonded strain gauges, the surface to be moved may be attached to a piston which is in turn attached to

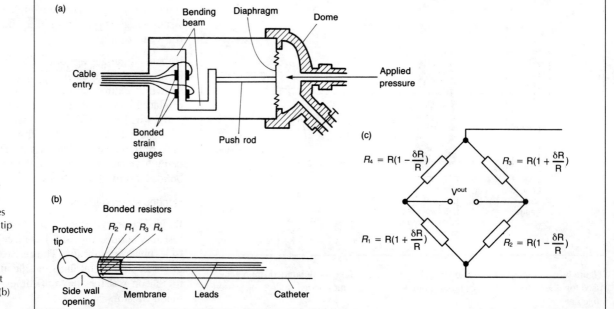

Figure 5.10
(a) External pressure transducer with bonded strain gauges
(b) Internal catheter tip pressure transducer using bonded strain gauges
(c) Equivalent circuit diagram for (a) and (b)

the centre of a rod fixed at both ends (known as a load cell), Figure 5.10(a) and (b). Attached to the rod are four strain gauges, two on the side to which the piston is attached, and two on the opposing side. As the diaphragm moves in and out the piston causes the rod to be bent towards or away from the diaphragm. This in turn causes the strain gauges on the inner side to be compressed or extended and the ones on the outer side to be extended or compressed respectively.

Sets of four strain gauges (bonded or unbonded) are used as the four arms of a Wheatstone bridge in order to increase the effect of the strain and to offset any temperature effects on resistance, Figure 5.10(c).

If the resistors are placed in the Wheatstone bridge arrangement shown in Figure 5.10(c), it can be shown using Kirchoff's laws that the output will be given by:

$$V_{out} = \frac{\delta R}{R} V_{in}$$

The output from the bridge will be of the order of millivolts per millimetre of mercury, and will need to be amplified before being recorded. The recorder may be a paper trace, a digital display or an oscilloscope used as a monitor.

Bonded strain gauges can be made to small dimensions and may be used in catheter tip measurements of pressure, Figure 5.10(b).

Capacitative transducers

Capacitative transducers can only be used with an alternating supply current, and only with varying pressures.

The capacitance C of two parallel plate electrodes each of area A and distance apart d with material between them of dielectric constant K is given by:

$$C \propto \frac{KA}{d}$$

If either the area A or the distance d is altered the value of the capacitance is altered proportionally. Transducers can be made which transfer the movement of a diaphragm or membrane so that either a cylinder plate is moved in or out thus altering A (Figure 5.11(a)) or one of the plates of a capacitor is moved thus altering d (Figure 5.11(b)).

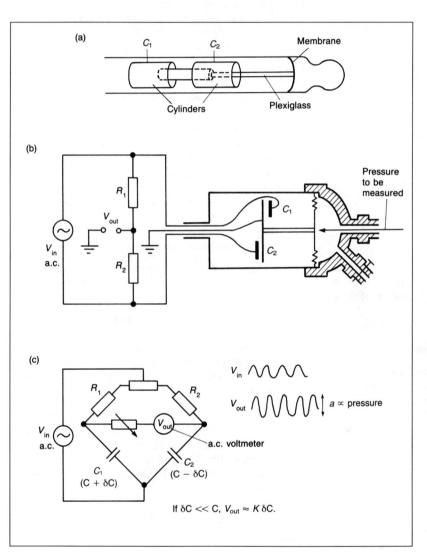

Figure 5.11 (a) Capacitance is proportional to area of plates. As area of C_1 increases, area of C_2 decreases.
(b) Capacative external pressure transducer
(c) Equivalent circuit for capacative transducer. The amplitude of V_{out} (a.c.) is proportional to the pressure.

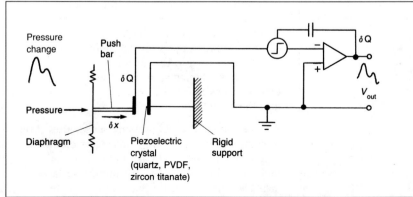

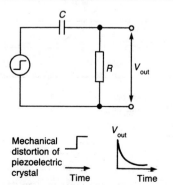

Figure 5.12
(a) Piezoelectric pressure transducer, used only with oscillating forces
(b) Equivalent circuit. This transducer is often used in determining Korotkoff sounds in pressure pulses – see page 45.

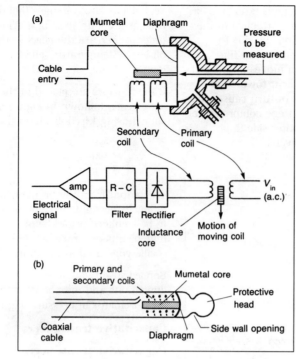

Figure 5.13
(a) External inductance pressure transducer and equivalent circuit
(b) Catheter tip inductance pressure transducer

In either case it is usual to make one plate common to two capacitors. If the common plate is moved one capacitor will increase in value by δC and the other will decrease in value by the same amount as the plate is moved. If the capacitors are used in a Wheatstone bridge formation (Figure 5.11(c)) the output will have an amplitude proportional to the displacement amplitude.

Piezoelectric pressure transducers

Piezoelectric pressure transducers (Figure 5.12(a)) are used where the pressure is continually changing with time. Piezoelectric crystals (see Chapter 13) have the property that when they are deformed (stretched or compressed), charges are produced on their surfaces so that a small potential difference exists across the crystal which varies

with the degree of deformation. The output of a piezoelectric transducer can be modelled as a voltage source in series with a capacitance.

When used in an amplifier as shown in Figure 5.12(a), the change in charge on the capacitance of the piezoelectric transducer is effectively transferred to the capacitor in the circuit. In this way the output of the system is inversely proportional to the deformation of the crystal.

Piezoelectric transducers are active components, that is they produce a voltage with no input voltage needed. A pressure of 10^4 Pa acting on 1 mm of material can produce 1 mV.

Inductance pressure transducers

Inductance pressure transducers use a small iron rod which is attached to a membrane or diaphragm. As the membrane moves the iron is pushed in or out of an electric coil, thus changing its inductance and the voltage output across its ends. Inductance pressure transducers have been used in external pressure domes (Figure 5.13(a)) and in catheter tip measurements of blood pressure (Figure 5.13(b)).

Internal and external pressure transducers

The types of pressure measurement mentioned above usually involve either an **internal** or an **external transducer**.

An **internal pressure transducer** is one in which a small pressure transducer is mounted in the tip of a catheter, the leads to the transducer being contained within the catheter, which is then inserted into the point of measurement within the patient.

The transducer is mounted on the underside of a membrane stretched over the cross-section of the catheter. Usually the catheter has a side-wall opening so that the pressure that is measured does not include the pressure due to the flow of fluids around it (blood or gastric juices, for example). Figure 5.13(b) shows an example of an internal induction pressure transducer.

Internal pressure transducers, such as that in Figure 5.13(b), are used to measure oesophageal pressures, pressures in the main arteries and, less often, bladder pressures. The response times of these transducers can be quite small and so rapid changes in pressure can be faithfully recorded. Transducers used in this way are quite delicate and can easily be damaged. In addition there is difficulty making the transducer small enough to fit into the catheter.

An alternative internal pressure sensor uses three to eight separate pressure transducers mounted within one catheter. The transducers are all mounted with their active membrane surfaces facing an opening in the side of the catheter.

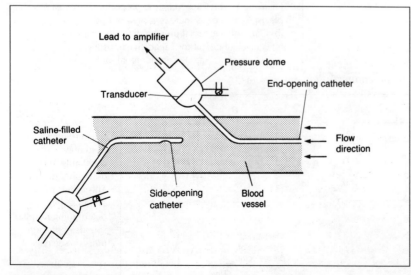

Figure 5.14   Side-hole and end-hole external pressure transducer

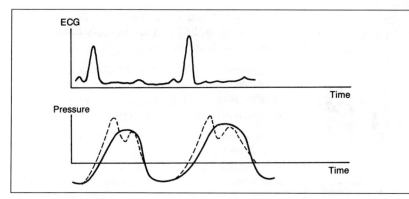

Figure 5.15   Undamped (dashed line) and damped (solid line) waveforms in an external pressure transducer

In an **external pressure transducer** there is an hydraulic connection (by means of a saline-filled catheter) between the pressure to be measured at the internal end of the catheter and the transducer at the external end. Figure 5.14 shows the arrangement used for an external pressure transducer.

The external end of the catheter is usually attached to a dome-shaped head with a diaphragm stretched across its diameter. The diaphragm may be attached to a **load cell** which has two resistors placed on its lower surface and two resistors placed on its upper surface. As the beam bends, the resistors on the upper surface increase in length and the two on the lower surface decrease in length. The resistors are arranged in the Wheatstone bridge arrangement as mentioned earlier in this chapter.

The diaphragm will have a resonant frequency (in the same way that wine glasses filled with water resonate at a particular frequency if struck). This means that if sudden pressure changes take place, the diaphragm will oscillate with a high initial amplitude which gradually reduces. This effect is often called 'ringing' and results in the pressure waveform being distorted (Figure 5.15).

There is a time lag between the pressure change at the catheter tip and the pressure change at the transducer end of the catheter. This reduces or **damps** the resonance of the diaphragm. The amount by which the resonance is damped depends on the size of the catheter and dome. The ideal damping occurs if the diameter of the connecting tube is small, the dome diameter is small and the catheter is stiff. Unfortunately as well as damping the resonance, this slows down the response time of the system which then cannot follow high-frequency fluctuations.

The pressure recorded by these devices will be relative to the distance between the pressure dome and the point of measurement. The pressure dome is usually placed at the height of the patient's heart. If only relative changes in pressure are of interest and not the absolute value of the pressure, the zero level may be set arbitrarily to zero at the start of the measurement period.

External pressure transducers are used for measurement of the pressure in the right atrium which is known as the **central venous pressure** or **CVP**. The central venous pressure is normally approximately zero when compared with atmospheric pressure. If large blood transfusions are given it increases sharply because of the increased flow of blood into the right atrium from the veins. If the heart beats faster, the CVP can be reduced sharply. These situations can occur in major operations, especially heart surgery, and so the CVP may be monitored during operations.

External pressure transducers are also used to measure intracranial (inside the skull) pressures, which can rise significantly following head injuries. In addition they are used to measure bladder pressures.

Blood pressure measurement

In Chapter 4, the action of the heart and the circulatory system were discussed. During the systolic part of the heart cycle the ventricles force blood through valves into two large arteries, the pulmonary artery which carries deoxygenated blood to the lungs, and the aorta which carries oxygenated blood to the body tissues. During systole the pressure in the pulmonary artery and the aorta is high (systolic pressure). When the heart is relaxed (diastole) the pulmonary and aortic valves close and the pressure in the pulmonary artery and aorta falls to a minimum (diastolic pressure). This cyclical change in pressure is known as the **pulsatility** of the pressure.

The oxygenated blood is circulated by the arterial system. The large arteries divide to form smaller and smaller arteries which terminate in the arterioles in the capillary beds. The venules connect with the arterioles in the capillary bed and in turn connect with larger and larger veins to return the blood to the heart.

In the capillary beds the oxygen is given up by the blood to be used by the tissues, and waste products diffuse into the blood (to be disposed of by the liver and kidney at a later stage). It is vital that blood should perfuse the capillaries or the tissues would soon die.

·The systolic pressure in the major arteries of a healthy young adult is about 120 mm Hg and the diastolic pressure 80 mm Hg. As the arteries become smaller, the pulsatility and mean pressure are both reduced slightly due both to the divisions at which some of the blood is reflected back, and due to the the fact that the walls of the blood vessels are fairly elastic and stretch. The arterioles reduce both pulsatility and mean pressure greatly. By the time the blood has reached the veins the pulsatility is nearly zero and the pressure is only a few mm Hg. The veins have non-return valves in them so that the blood cannot flow backwards. By

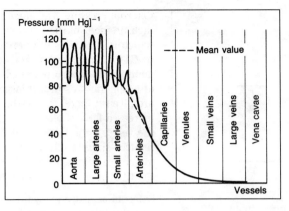

Figure 5.16 Blood pressures in different parts of the circulatory system (after Guyton)

The cyclical changes which occur in the main arteries near to the heart are strongly related to the action of the heart valves.

The pressures in the circulatory system are measured relative to a fixed pressure. The fixed pressure is taken to be the CVP and, as seen previously, this is normally approximately zero.

When standing, the hydrostatic pressure of the blood in the veins is dependent on the height above or below the right atrium at which the measurement is made, as is shown in Figure 5.17.

the time the blood has reached the large veins the pressure is nearly zero.

Figure 5.16 shows the variation of pulsatility and pressure for arteries and veins in a healthy person.

The way in which the blood pressure changes during one cycle can give the doctor information about how that patient's heart is functioning.

Indirect blood pressure measurement – the sphygmomanometer

The methods of measuring pressure so far described have all used transducers which produce a voltage output proportional to a pressure applied directly to the transducer. These are known as **direct measurements**.

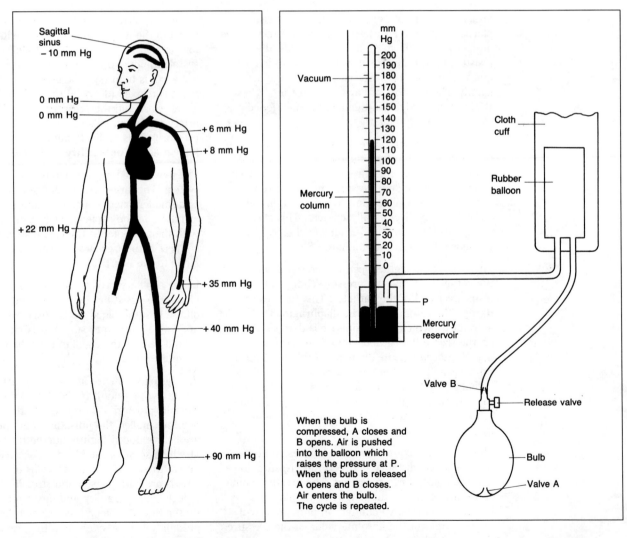

Figure 5.17 The effect of the hydrostatic pressure on the venous pressures when standing

Figure 5.18 Indirect pressure measurement – the sphygmomanometer

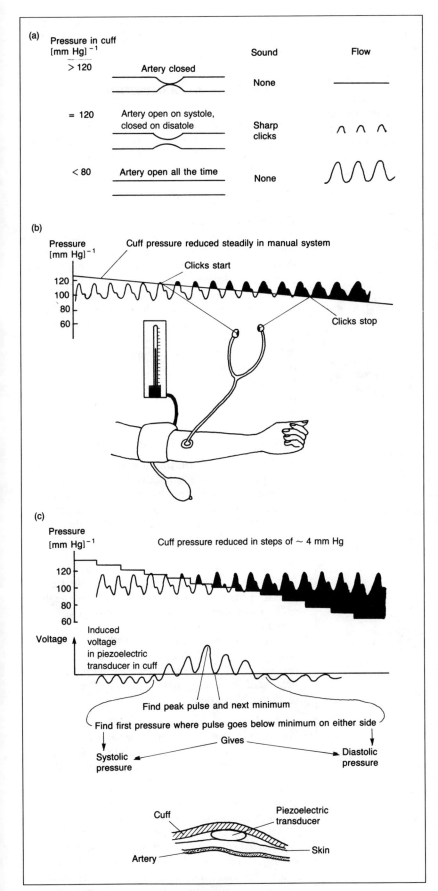

The method of measuring pressure described in this section does not apply the pressure to a transducer, but rather applies a pressure to the arm of more than sufficient value to stop the blood flow. The operator can tell if the blood flow is stopped by listening to the pulse using a stethoscope.

The most simple method of measuring blood pressure is by the use of the **sphygmomanometer** in conjunction with a stethoscope. This indirect method of measuring blood pressure is explained below.

The sphygmomanometer, Figure 5.18, consists of a cuff of material inside which is a flat rubber balloon. Rubber tubing connects the balloon directly to a mercury manometer and via the one-way valve B to a rubber bulb. The rubber bulb also has a connection to the atmosphere by means of another one-way valve, A. Squeezing the bulb increases the pressure inside, closing valve A and opening valve B. The pressure in the tubing is thus increased and the value is shown on the manometer. When the operator stops squeezing the bulb, the pressure inside is reduced, causing valve B to close and valve A to open. Air therefore rushes into the bulb from the atmosphere, ready to repeat the procedure and raise the pressure more if required.

The cuff containing the balloon is wrapped round the upper arm at about the level of the heart. The cuff is inflated as above to a pressure of 200 mm Hg, which is well above the systolic pressure. Meanwhile a stethoscope is placed over the main artery at the elbow, the brachial artery. The pressure in the bulb and tubing system is then gradually reduced by opening a screw valve in the side of the bulb.

As the pressure is reduced the operator listens to the sounds from the stethoscope. When the external pressure supplied by the cuff is high, the artery is pressed shut and there is no sound. As the cuff pressure falls just below the systolic pressure a series of clicks is heard as the artery opens briefly with the pressure from each pulse of blood, and then clicks shut as the pressure within the artery falls below the external pressure, Figure 5.19. These clicks are called Korotkoff sounds.

The series of clicks disappears when the external pressure is reduced below the diastolic pressure, as the artery then remains open throughout the cardiac cycle. By observing the pressure reading on the manometer as the clicks start and end, the systolic and diastolic pressures respectively can be found.

Thus the pressure has been determined by applying an external pressure and noting the value of that pressure when particular sounds occur. This is why the method determines blood pressure *indirectly*.

Figure 5.19   (a) Korotkoff sounds in the sphygmomanometer
(b) Manual blood pressure measurement using sphygmomanometer and stethoscope
(c) Automatic method of measuring blood pressure

It should be remembered that while the cuff is inflated the blood supply to the lower arm and hand has been cut off! Speed and accuracy in using a sphygmomanometer are therefore required so that the flow can be restored as quickly as possible.

Automatic versions of the sphygmomanometer are now being widely introduced onto hospital wards. The cuff is placed, as in the manual version, on the patient's upper arm. The pressure within the balloon is automatically pumped up at preset time intervals (for example hourly). The pressure of the cuff is then reduced in steps. At each step a piezoelectric pressure transducer converts the oscillations in pressure caused by the pulsing artery into voltage signals which are recorded. The average amplitude of the pulsations at each pressure level is recorded and follows a pattern, as shown in Figure 5.19(c).

The positions on the curve corresponding to the systolic and diastolic pressures are marked, being the first low amplitudes on either side of the peak amplitude.

A microcomputer system analyses the amplitudes and calculates the systolic and diastolic pressures, which are then indicated on a digital display.

The system can be programmed to sound a warning alarm if dangerously low or high values occur. The system will also display the pulse rate, and can be set to alarm if this is outside preset values. This type of automatic system is especially useful for constant monitoring of patients who have just had major operations. It avoids having to wake patients to take blood pressure, and saves time for nursing staff.

Automatic systems can also be used with a Doppler ultrasound device as the method of registering the blood flow.

Blood flow measurement

Many techniques have been used to measure blood flow. In this section two techniques – Doppler and electromagnetic flowmetry – are described. Both in fact measure blood velocity.

The Doppler flowmeter

The **Doppler flowmeter** consists of a small ultrasound transducer as outlined in Chapter 13. Ultrasound waves at a frequency of 3–5 MHz are directed towards the blood vessel to be investigated. Part of the incident sound is reflected by the blood cells back to the transducer. If the blood is flowing away from the transducer, the frequency of the reflected signal is lower than that of the original signal, because of the Doppler effect. The frequency difference between reflected and transmitted signals is proportional to the velocity of the blood. The reverse will occur if the blood is flowing towards the transducer, when the reflected signal will have a higher frequency.

The electromagnetic flowmeter

The **electromagnetic flowmeter** works upon the principle that an electromotive force is produced when a conductor is moved in a magnetic field. Figure 5.20(a) shows the potential u generated when a wire of length l is moved perpendicular to a field of flux B at velocity v:

$$u = Blv$$

If the wire is removed but a flowing conductor is placed in the field, each element of a cross-section of the blood can be considered to be the wire moving in the field. Thus the element a–b in Figure 5.20(b) will produce an e.m.f. of Blv. However, smaller elements such as c–d in the diagram will produce smaller potentials. Overall the potential generated is given by BDv_{mean}, where D is the diameter of the pipe.

In the flowmeter considered here, the moving conductor is the blood. The flowmeter containing an electromagnet is placed around the blood vessel to be investigated, as indicated in Figure 5.20(c).

When blood flows in the vessel, an electric potential proportional to the velocity of the flow is generated in the circuit within the probe and is detected using a meter. Changes occurring in less than 0.01 s can be detected. Although the technique is quite accurate, one major disadvantage is that the coil must be positioned very closely around the blood vessel to be investigated. It is therefore only of use during operative procedures, when the vessel can be exposed.

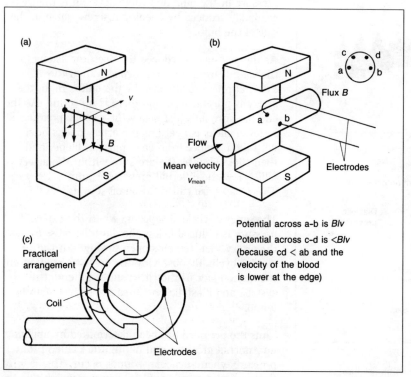

Figure 5.20   The electromagnetic flowmeter

Other methods of blood flow measurement

Blood flow can be measured, or at least estimated, using other techniques. These techniques, using radionuclide imaging or M-mode ultrasonics, have been applied particularly to the measurement of blood flow through the heart.

Transducers for other parameters

There is a wide range of transducers for measurements other than temperature, pressure and flow. Although you may not need to remember all of these, you should be aware that the number is large. A few are described below.

pH measurement

The acidity or alkalinity of a solution is measured on a scale of 0 to 12, with values above 7 being rated as acidic and values below as alkaline. The value 7 itself is neutral.

It is necessary to be able to determine the acidity of parts of the gastrointestinal tract to find out whether the function of the tract is normal.

Most pH transducers are based on the effect of hydrogen ions on one electrode of an electrolytic cell, causing an alteration in the electric potential produced by the cell. The concentration of hydrogen ions is directly related to the pH of the cell and can be related in turn to the output voltage of the cell.

Figure 5.21(a) shows a typical electrode for use in the oesophagus and stomach.

The glass membrane forms the electrode sensitive to pH. The internal electrode is made of silver with a silver chloride coating. There is an internal buffer solution. An internal reference electrode is used to give absolute pH measurements. This uses a silver/silver chloride electrode in an electrolytic solution of potassium chloride. Figure 5.21(b) shows an equivalent cell.

One of the uses of the pH transducer is to determine the acidity in the oesophagus. Normally the pH value in a healthy oesophagus is of the order of 6–7. The pH value in the stomach is normally 1–3. If the sphincter muscle separating the stomach from the oesophagus is not functioning correctly, acid may be regurgitated from the stomach back into the oesophagus. Since the oesophagus does not have the same protective lining as the stomach, large ulcerations can occur at the base of the oesophagus. Normally measurements of pH are made continuously for 24 hours as Figure 5.21(c) shows, so that the effects of meals, sleeping and moving around can be recorded.

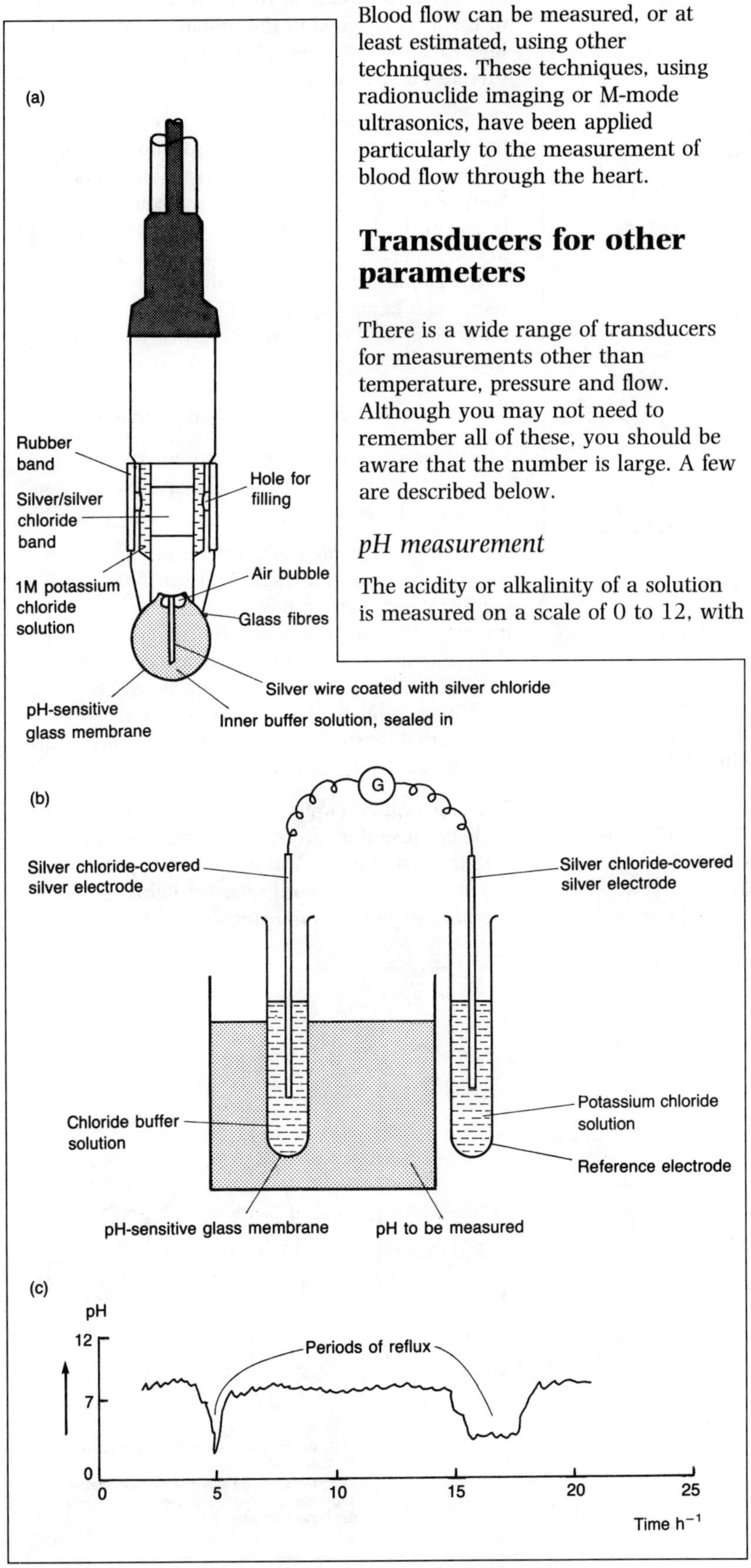

Gas-sensitive probes

Transducers can be made which give an electrical output which is proportional to the pressure of a specific gas, for example oxygen or carbon dioxide.

A typical oxygen transducer for continous monitoring is shown in Figure 5.22. The transducer consists of a central platinum cathode and a silver/silver choride anode. Both anode and cathode are coated in an electrolyte. The catheter tip is covered in an oxygen permeable membrane (PVC or PTFE). The membrane allows oxygen to diffuse through it and an electrochemical reaction takes place near the cathode, producing a small current. A complete circuit is made by connecting the anode and the cathode to an external meter by passing wires down one channel of a two-channel catheter to a small stabilised power supply. In this way an electrical current of the order of 10 nA is generated, which is proportional to the amount of oxygen diffusing through the membrane. This

Figure 5.21 (a) pH electrode for use in the oesophagus and stomach
(b) Equivalent circuit for pH probe (c) 24-hour trace of pH in oesophagus

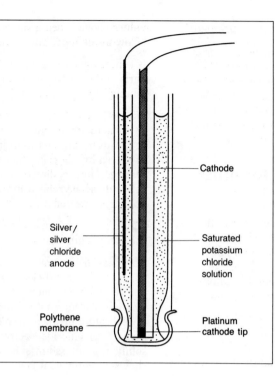

Figure 5.22
Oxygen transducer

current has to be amplified greatly before it can be measured.

The main difficulty with this method is that clots may form over the transducer at the tip of the catheter, even when a special solution is used to help prevent this.

Oxygen concentration measurements are often made on the blood of premature babies. The measurement the partial pressure of oxygen, pO_2, can be made continuously either on the skin

surface (transcutaneous measurements), or by placing a transducer at the tip of a catheter placed in the arterial blood in the umbilical tube, or at intervals from samples taken from the umbilical tube to the laboratory.

Continuous measurement of the arterial oxygen in the umbilical tube is made in order to determine the percentage of oxygen necessary in the neonatal baby's air supply. If the partial pressure of oxygen is low in the baby's blood, the percentage of oxygen in the supply is increased. There is an upper limit to the pO_2 of 80%, for above this level the baby's retina can be damaged, causing blindness. The lower limit is of course the percentage of oxygen in the air, ~21%.

Plethysmography and pulse oximeters

Plethysmography is the measurement of pressure within a part of a body. The light plethysmograph measures the pressure pulse.

The light plethysmograph, shown in Figure 5.23(a), consists of a small light source (a light-emitting diode) and a means of detecting light intensity (a photodetector). The current flowing in the photodetector circuit is proportional to the intensity of the light falling upon its surface. Light is emitted from the diode and reflected or transmitted by the blood onto the detector. Figure 5.23(b) shows the circuit.

The capillaries change shape during the cardiac cycle because they are stretched more during systole than diastole. If the detector is placed beside the emitter it will record reflected light. As the capillary expands its top surface will be closer to

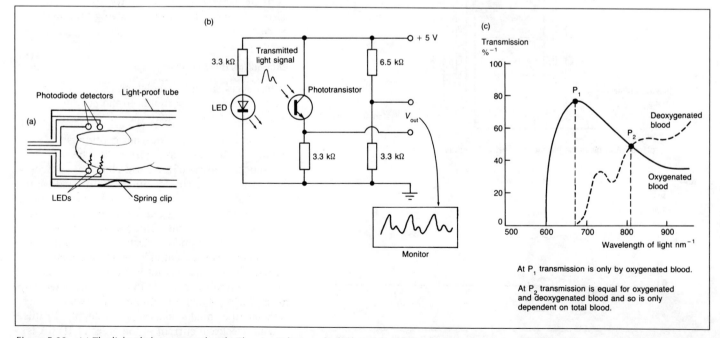

Figure 5.23   (a) The light plethysomograph   (b) The circuit for one diode/detector   (c) Percentage transmission of light of different wavelengths through oxygenated and deoxygenated blood. If the two light sources have wavelengths of 640 and 805 nm, then the ratio of their transmission gives a measure of the blood oxygenation.

the emitter and detector and the intensity of light falling upon the photodetector will increase.

If the detector is placed so that it records light transmitted through the skin (say through the finger or ear lobe), the intensity of light falling on it will vary as the amount of blood in the capillaries. There will be more blood in the capillaries during systole than diastole.

In either case it is found that the amount of light falling on the photodetector is proportional to the pressure changes during the cardiac cycle. The detector thus follows the changes in the blood pressure during the cardiac cycle. The frequency at which the waveform is repeated is a measure of the pulse and its amplitude a measure of the strength of the pulse.

The proportion of light transmitted by the blood depends on the wavelength of the light and the percentage of haemoglobin in it which is oxygenated, Figure 5.23(c). Two wavelengths of light are used, and a detector for each wavelength. The percentage of the blood which is oxygenated is proportional to the ratio of the transmitted intensities of the two wavelengths. The output from one of the detectors also gives the same information as the reflective photoplethysmograph, the pulse rate. Since both the pulse rate and percentage of oxygen in the blood are measured in this machine it is called a **pulse oximeter**.

Pulse oximeters are widely used in operating theatres, intensive care units and special care baby units for monitoring the oxygen in the blood.

Summary

1. Temperature can be measured by mercury-in-glass thermometers, thermistors or thermocouples. The latter two are used in conjunction with Wheatstone bridges to improve their accuracy.

2. Pressure is measured directly internally by using detectors in the tips of catheters or directly externally by using dome-headed transducers. Changes in electrical resistance, capacitance, inductance and the piezoelectric effect are used to measure pressure changes. Greater accuracy is achieved by the use of Wheatsone bridges. Indirect measurements of blood pressure are made externally with a sphygmomanometer.

3. Flow is measured by the electromotive force or Doppler ultrasound.

4. Other physiological measurements include pH and oxygen monitoring and photoplethysmography.

Questions

1. Why are Wheatstone bridges often used to measure changes in resistance? Calculate the change output potential of the Wheatstone bridge shown in Figure 5.3 when there is a change in pressure of 0.02 Pa if there is change in resistance of 1% when the pressure changes by 1 Pa and $V_{in} = 10$ V.

2. What is a transducer? Name four kinds of transducer used for measuring changes in pressure.

3. Why is a catheter tip pressure transducer better at measuring pressure changes during open heart surgery than an external dome pressure transducer?

4. What temperature would you expect to find 8 cm inside a living person's body? How would you expect this to differ from that measured on the skin of the hand of a patient:

   a) who was just recovering from major surgery
   b) in a hot country?

5. Why are thermistors more often used for temperature measurement in hospital equipment than thermocouples?

6. What method would you use to measure the blood flow of a patient coming to a vascular clinic with suspected hardening of the arteries (plaque)? Describe the principles of the method.

6 OPTICAL SYSTEMS IN MEDICINE

Endoscopy

The word **endoscopy** means 'look within' (from the Greek words 'endon' = 'within' and 'scopeo' = 'to look into'). Endoscopes are flexible tubes containing optical fibres, which are inserted within orifices (openings) of the body in order to look at internal surfaces without the need for surgery. For example, endoscopes are inserted via the mouth and oesophagus into the stomach to look at the lining of the stomach if it is suspected that a patient might have ulcers.

In order to view an internal surface it is necessary to illuminate it with light, and to transmit the image of the surface back to the operator. Bundles of optical fibres are used for both these tasks. These bundles are known as **light guides** and can be used even when bent through several angles.

Light guides use the principle of the **critical angle** which exists between two transparent adjacent media of different refractive index. This property is an extension of Snell's law which is summarised briefly below.

Snell's law

Referring to Figure 6.1(a), a ray of light is incident at an angle i to the normal on the boundary of two media of refractive index n_1 and n_2 respectively. If n_2 is lower than n_1 most of the ray is refracted at an angle r to the normal and a small amount is reflected. The relationship between the angle of incidence i and the angle of refraction r is given by:

$$\frac{\sin i}{\sin r} = \frac{n_2}{n_1} \quad \text{according to Snell's law}$$

Critical angle and total internal reflection

As the angle of incidence i in Figure 6.1(a) is increased, the angle of refraction r is also increased until eventually it is 90° (see Figure 6.1(b) and (c)). At this point the refracted ray just skims the surface of the boundary of the two media. The angle of incidence at which this happens is known as the **critical angle** which is denoted here as i_c.

If the angle of incidence is increased still further, all of the ray is now reflected from the boundary and total internal reflection takes place, Figure 6.1(d).

Optical properties of rods

Consider a rod of transparent medium of refractive index n_1 surrounded (clad) by another of a lower refractive index n_2 so that its cross-section is as shown in Figure 6.2(a). It can be seen that rays of light incident on the rod–cladding interface at an angle greater than the critical angle can be reflected from side to side and emerge at the other end with very little loss of intensity.

If the rod is now surrounded by another medium of refractive index n_0, a light ray incident at the interface with the rod at an angle of incidence β with the normal to the surface will be refracted away from the normal at angle r. As β decreases, r decreases, and i increases. Hence there will be a minimum angle β_{oc} corresponding to the critical angle i_c, Figure 6.2(b).

Considering now the real case which is in three dimensions, it can be seen that there is a cone of

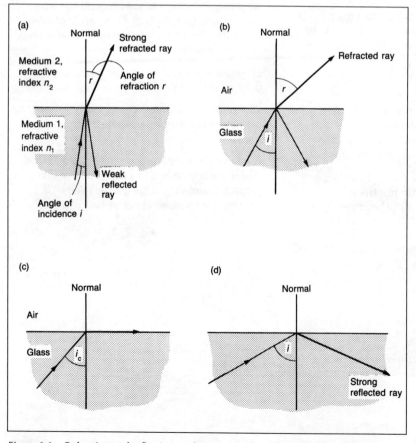

Figure 6.1   Refraction and reflection at glass–air interface for increasing angles of incidence

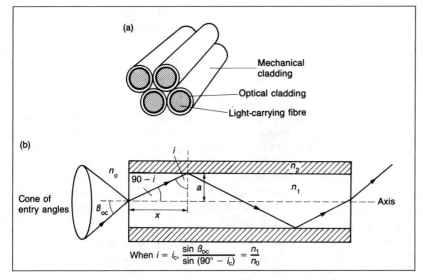

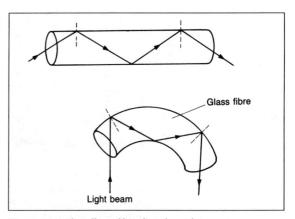

Figure 6.2   Reflection in a rod clad in a material of lower refractive index

entry angles within which any light ray must fall if it is to be totally internally reflected when incident at the rod–cladding interface.

If the rod is now made to curve, as shown in Figure 6.3, the angle at which the ray is incident on the boundary changes each time the ray is incident at the boundary. If the critical angle is not exceeded at every one of these points the ray will be refracted out of the fibre.

Optical properties of fibres

Optical fibres are made of rods which have a solid core made of glass (or polymethacrylate) with a cladding of glass (or another polymer) of lower refractive index. They use the principle of total internal reflection as discussed above (see also Figures 6.1 and 6.2) to guide the light.

In Figure 6.2(b) it can be seen that there is a critical angle β_{oc} for the light beam entering the fibre in order that total internal reflection (which occurs when the angle of incidence $>i_c$) takes place at the interface between core and cladding. Using the principle of Snell's law at the two surfaces medium-to-core and core-to-cladding it can be seen that this angle is given by:

$$\beta_{oc} = \sin^{-1}\{n_1{}^2 - n_2{}^2\}^{\frac{1}{2}}/n_0$$

where n_0, n_1 and n_2 are refractive indices for the medium surrounding the rod, the rod glass and the cladding glass respectively.

$(n_1{}^2 - n_2{}^2)^{\frac{1}{2}}$ is defined as the **numerical aperture** NA of the optical fibre and is used in many calculations.

Typical values of n_1 lie between 1.55 and 1.63 and of n_2 lie between 1.45 and 1.53. n_0 is usually equal to 1. The critical angle β_{oc} will thus take values between 14° and 50°.

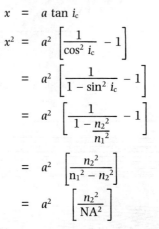

Figure 6.3   The effect of bending the rod

If the incident angle β_0 is larger than the critical angle β_{oc}, light energy is refracted out of the interface between core and cladding and suffers multiple reflections. In this case the light energy is not transmitted down the length of the fibre. If on the other hand the angle at which the light enters the rod is less than the critical angle, the beam undergoes total internal reflection each time it is reflected from the sides of the rod. Then the beam emerges at the other end of the rod after many reflections, having lost some of its original energy. In fact it loses about 0.04% of the light received at each reflecting point.

In passing it should be noted that total internal reflection could be achieved in one rod without cladding provided that the surrounding medium was of lower refractive index. However, in a large bundle of rods there would be points of contact along the surfaces at which light could be lost from the system if no cladding was used.

Losses at each reflection

To find the number of reflections for a ray incident at the critical angle consider Figure 6.2(b). The distance $2x$ down the length of the tube between successive reflections is given by:

$$x = a \tan i_c$$

$$x^2 = a^2 \left[\frac{1}{\cos^2 i_c} - 1\right]$$

$$= a^2 \left[\frac{1}{1 - \sin^2 i_c} - 1\right]$$

$$= a^2 \left[\frac{1}{1 - \dfrac{n_2{}^2}{n_1{}^2}} - 1\right]$$

$$= a^2 \left[\frac{n_2{}^2}{n_1{}^2 - n_2{}^2}\right]$$

$$= a^2 \left[\frac{n_2{}^2}{NA^2}\right]$$

Taking square roots:

$$x = a \frac{n_2}{NA}$$

The number N of reflections for a ray incident at the critical angle for a fibre of length L and with core diameter $2a$ is given by:

$$N = \frac{L}{2x} \qquad \text{if } 2x \text{ is the distance between reflections}$$

$$= \frac{L\,NA}{2an_2}$$

The intensity I after N reflections is:

$$I = R^N$$

where R is the fraction of the initial intensity of light reflected at each interface. For a typical endoscope of 1.0 m in length and rods of 100 μm diameter with $n_2 = 1.45$ and NA = 0.744 the loss will be 64%. The fraction of the initial intensity transmitted for different values of reflectance R and rods of different dimensions is shown in Figure 6.4. It can be seen that although the loss is very small at each reflection, after 1000 or more reflections that occur in a typical endoscope, the total loss is very large.

Losses on entrance and exit

At the entrance and exit of the rod, light energy is partly reflected (Fresnel reflection). The proportion R_f of the incident light reflected in this way (the **reflectance**) is given by:

$$R_f = [(n_1 - n_0)/(n_1 + n_0)]^2$$

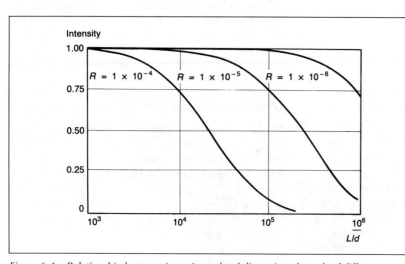

Figure 6.4   Relationship between intensity and rod dimensions for rods of different refractive indices

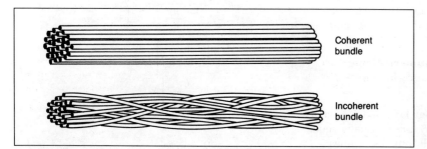

Figure 6.5   Coherent and incoherent bundles of glass fibres

This loss can be reduced by applying antireflection multilayer coatings to both sides.

Limitation on bending radius

There are mechanical limits on the bending radius, but the mechanical cladding usually prevents this being exceeded. The bending radius decreases as the thickness increases. Polymer fibres are usually thicker than glass ones but have greater flexibility and so the range of bending radius values which can be achieved is the same. The bending radius for a bundle of fibres of 4.5 mm diameter is 64 mm.

Many fibres are needed to view an orifice such as the gastrointestinal tract. Most bundles contain 20 000–30 000 fibres.

Mechanical protection

In addition to the optical cladding, a layer of mechanical cladding is applied to protect the fibre from fracture. The fibre bundle also has a PVC jacket for protection. Despite this 20–30 fibres per bundle are usually damaged in manufacture, and more will become damaged with the flexure that occurs in use.

Coherent and incoherent bundles

There are two forms of bundles of glass fibres, **coherent** and **incoherent** bundles. Figure 6.5 illustrates the two kinds.

Coherent bundles are made up of fibres which have their ends placed in the same spatial order relative to each other at either end of the bundle. For example, imagine a cross-section of the bundle at one end with axes x and y. The position of the nth fibre is given by (x_n, y_n). Its position in the cross-section at the other end of the bundle will also be given by (x_n, y_n).

Incoherent bundles have no such particular arrangement of fibres; their fibres are randomly positioned at either end.

When an image falls on one end of a bundle it causes light to travel down the fibres, forming a pattern of dots at the other end. In a coherent bundle the pattern of dots faithfully reproduces the original image. In the incoherent bundle the dots are randomly positioned and no clear image is produced at the far end.

Coherent bundles are expensive to make, so in endoscopes an incoherent bundle may be used as the light guide which transmits light down the endoscope, and a coherent bundle to transmit the image back up to the observer.

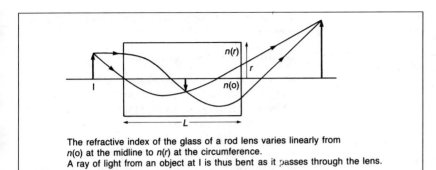

The refractive index of the glass of a rod lens varies linearly from
n(o) at the midline to *n*(r) at the circumference.
A ray of light from an object at I is thus bent as it passes through the lens.

Figure 6.6   The refractive index of the glass of a rod lens varies linearly from *n* (0) at the midline to *n* (r) at the circumference. A ray of light from an object at I is thus bent as it passes through the lens.

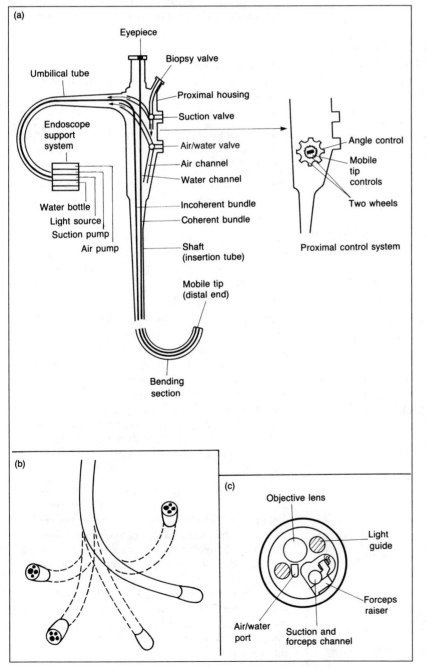

Figure 6.7   (a) Structure of an endoscope   (b) Mobile tip positions
(c) End-on view of mobile tip

The objective and ocular lenses

The endoscope also needs an objective lens at one end of the bundle (the tip), and an eyepiece or ocular lens at the other. The objective lens focuses the image onto the tip end of the bundle. The ocular lens transmits the light from the observer's end into the eye, and at the same time magnifies the image. The image can be focused by adjustments to the ocular and objective lenses. Figure 6.6 shows the type of compound lens used for the objective and ocular lenses in an endoscope (in this case, a laparoscope).

Structure of the endoscope

The endoscope is composed of six sections along its length: the distal end, bending section, insertion tube, proximal control section, umbilical tube and support system. Figure 6.7(a) shows an endoscope connected to a support system which includes a light supply unit.

The proximal housing is a rigid plastic and metal structure containing the eyepiece, focusing controls, tip controls and valves for hand control of suction, air and water supply.

The insertion tube

The bundles of fibres are all contained within a flexible shaft known as the **insertion tube**, as are the other channels (see below). The flexible shaft terminates in the tip at one end and the proximal housing at the other.

The tip of the endoscope can be be manoeuvred by means of a system of four wires attached to two wheels in the proximal housing. The tip can be moved up, down, to the left and to the right, being capable of bending through 180°. In this way all the organ to be studied can be imaged, as shown in Figure 6.7(b).

The endoscope contains other channels besides the optical ones, as Figure 6.7(c) shows. Air and water channels are use for flushing and inflating the organ under view. There is also a suction channel to clear fluids from the field of view.

There is also a means for raising a biopsy attachment, so that small samples of diseased tissue can be cut from the surface and transported back up the endoscope. Such samples are then put in glass containers and sent to the pathology laboratory for analysis.

Recently it has become possible to insert a laser into the insertion tube. The laser can be used as a thermal device for coagulation of blood vessels, for example in ulcers. It can also be used for burning cancerous tissue as found, for example, in the oesophagus. Argon and neodymium–yttrium aluminium garnet (Nd–YAG) lasers are used in endoscopy (see pages 55–6).

The umbilical tube

The tubular structure which is at right angles to the main body of the endoscope and which conveys air, water, light and suction from an external support system to the fibrescope is known as the **umbilical tube**.

The support system

The support system includes a light source, water supply, water suction, a flash lamp and a small camera. The light has to be intense enough to allow for the losses down the tube, but must not heat the tissue under study. Before the advent of fibre optics in endoscopy the light source had to be at the distal end of the endoscope and could cause burns. With fibre optics the light source is in a separate housing so the light supplied to the proximal end of the endoscope and any infrared light are lost from the system, because the critical angle for these wavelengths is larger than that for the other optical wavelegths. For both these reasons the sources of light are said to be 'cold'. High-power xenon short-arc or halogen lamps are used as light sources. The xenon arc lamp can be used continuously for viewing or pulsed to provide a flash for taking images with the camera attachment.

Uses of endoscopes

Endoscopes are used in the gastrointestinal tract for the purpose of viewing the tract, taking biopsies and in some operative techniques. Examples of operative techniques are removal of polyps by diathermy, see Figure 6.8. Diathermy is a technique whereby a high-intensity alternating electric current at radio frequency (400 kHz –1 MHz) passes between electrodes, forming intense heat for a short period of time. The heat destroys tissue in the immediate area and at the same time seals off blood vessels by coagulation of the blood. Other uses of diathermy include dilation of the oesophagus (after swallowing bleach or with cancerous growths), coagulation of blood vessels and removal of cancerous tissue by means of laser therapy.

Location of endoscopic studies

Endoscopes are employed in the upper gastrotintestinal tract – the oesophageous, stomach and duodenum (**gastroscopy**) and the rectum and the colon (**colonoscopy**). Other less common endoscopes are the **enteroscopes** used for looking at the surfaces of the small intestine, the **laparoscopes** which are used to look at internal organs through a puncture in the abdomen and the **choleochoscopes** for viewing the bile channels to make sure gallstones have not been left behind. Endoscopes are also used to look at the nasal tract and the bronchial tree (**bronchofibrescopes**).

Case study

A typical case for the use of an endoscope would be for a patient with a suspected ulcer in the stomach or jejunem. The patient would commonly have pain just before or during meals.

An out-patient appointment would be made for the patient who would be starved for 8 hours prior to the procedure.

Before the endoscope is used it must be sterilised, often by immersing it in a bucket of disinfectant solution.

The patient lies on his or her side on a stretcher trolley, having been given sedation three hours before. The back of the throat may also be sprayed with anaesthetic. The patient is conscious, feeling discomfort but no pain.

A tube with a tooth grip is placed in the mouth so that the endoscope can be inserted through it. This protects the endoscope from possible damage if the patient bit on it. The patient is asked to swallow to ease the passage of the endoscope down the oesophagus. As the tube is passed down, the physician looks through the eyepiece or at a monitor displaying the image. From time to time water or air is blown through the endoscope to clear mucous and other fluids away from the endoscope tip.

At each point the physician turns the endoscope tip in all directions to examine the surface of the oesophagus. Note is taken of the length inserted which can be found from the divisions on the outside of the endoscope. The endoscope is moved into the stomach and again all the surfaces are viewed. As the endoscope is moved the physician records any findings on tape. If some remedial action is appropriate, such as laser treatment of the damaged surface, then the appropriate tool is inserted in the endoscope and the desired operation takes place.

Finally the endoscope is removed and re-sterilised before being used on the next patient. The time for

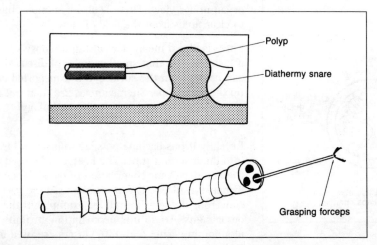

Figure 6.8   The use of an endoscope for the removal of polyps

the procedure typically takes half an hour. The patient may be given a course of treatment and a further endoscopy may be undertaken to assess how well the treatment is working.

Questions

1. Explain how total internal reflection is used in endoscopy. What is the critical angle for a glass 1/ glass 2 interface if the refractive index of glass 1 is 1.5 and the refractive index of glass 2 is 1.3? What is the critical angle of entry from air for this system?

2. Explain how optical fibres can be used to transmit pictures of the stomach to an observer. What is the advantage of using endoscopes rather than conventional surgery? Name two cases where a laparoscope could be used.

Lasers

The light from a LASER (light amplification by stimulated emission of radiation) has particular properties which lead to a variety of uses, including some in medicine.

The light is essentially **monochromatic** in nature – it is emitted either as one single wavelength, or as a number of single wavelengths, depending on the source material. This is very different from most common light sources, which emit light over a wide range of wavelengths. The stimulated emission process also produces **coherent** light – that is, all the light waves are in phase. Again, this is different from all other light sources, where the phases of the light waves are random.

These properties, in conjunction with the small beam areas achievable, lead to very intense light sources which have such a high energy density that they are capable of disrupting the structure of the material at which they are aimed.

Medical applications

Various types of materials have been made which produce lasers, and the different wavelengths of radiation that result can be used in a variety of medical applications. Some examples are given in Table 6.1.

Table 6.1

Laser material	Wavelength	Application
helium–neon	633 nm (visible red)	alignment (low power)
carbon dioxide	10.6 μm (far infrared)	general surgery
argon–ion	488 nm (blue) 515 nm (green)	ophthalmology (eye 'surgery')
neodymium–YAG	1.06 μm (near infrared)	gastro-enterology ophthalmology
dye	577 nm (yellow-orange)	birthmark removal

Helium–neon lasers are usually low-power devices. Their most frequent use is when coupled with higher-power infrared lasers so that the beam path of these otherwise invisible lasers can be seen. They are also used as alignment devices in radiotherapy, or as pointers during slide lectures. In these applications the lasers must be of very low power so that there is no possibility of hazard, particularly to the eye.

The **carbon dioxide lasers** used in surgical applications emit between 20 W and 100 W of laser power. The exact power level is usually adjustable by the surgeon for the particular circumstance and patient. At this far infrared wavelength the power is all absorbed within the first 0.2 mm of body tissue, and in particular by the water present in the cells. Soft tissue, which contains a high water content, will therefore be rapidly vaporised. The laser beam can be used to remove tissue near the surface, or as a cutting instrument by repeated application in one area.

One advantage of using a laser-based technique is that the large amount of heat produced in the surrounding tissue has the effect of shrinking and blocking the flow through the small blood vessels in the area. This means that the laser treatment produces much less blood loss than the equivalent knife-based surgical technique.

The most common application for carbon dioxide lasers occurs in gynaecology, for the treatment of early cervical cancer. The procedure, in which the largely surface-lying tumours are vaporised, can usually be successfully done on an outpatient basis. This is much less traumatic for the patient than a standard surgical operation, which tends to lead to a much longer stay in hospital.

Argon–ion lasers are normally used at a power level of approximately 5 W. The blue and green light produced by the laser is highly scattered by body tissues, and only diffuses to a depth of approximately 0.5 mm before being completely absorbed.

This type of laser is normally used in ophthalmology, and is particularly useful in the treatment of detached retinas. A fine beam is further focused by the lens of the patient's eye to a small spot on the retina. The heat produced at the spot welds the retina back in place, and repeated 'shots' successfully re-attach the retina. A similar technique is also used to block and destroy small blood vessels that can occur in the eyes of some diabetics, and which would otherwise result in progressive blindness.

The **neodymium–YAG laser** is formed by doping crystals of yttrium aluminium garnet with neodymium ions. Under suitable conditions, lasers can be produced with power levels between 60 W and 100 W, again adjustable by the surgeon. The near infrared radiation produced by this laser is

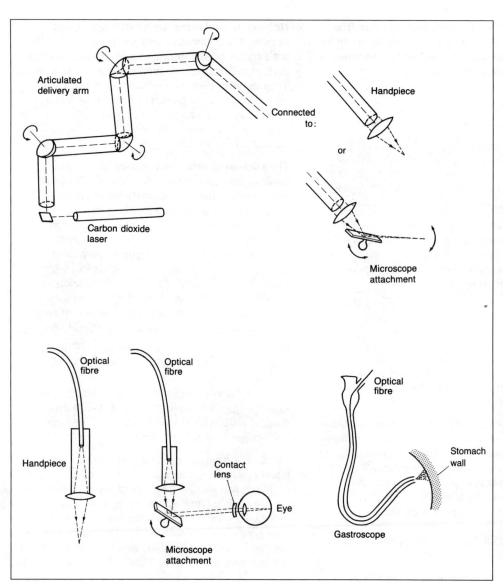

Figure 6.9   Articulated arm and optical fibre systems for delivery of laser treatments

disappear over a number of treatments.

Laser delivery systems

For any of the laser applications just described, one of the most crucial aspects is the accurate delivery of the laser beam to the particular part of the patient undergoing treatment. A variety of delivery systems have been devised, and are outlined in Figure 6.9.

The carbon dioxide laser systems commonly use an articulated arm composed of a number of tubular linear sections with mirrors at the joints. The joints can be rotated to enable the final output point of the laser to be accurately moveable in three dimensions.

The argon–ion and neodymium–YAG laser systems usually employ optical fibres to carry the beam to a suitable endpoint. This optical fibre system cannot be used with the carbon dioxide laser as its radiation is absorbed within the fibre materials.

For the direct surgical and dermatological applications, a handpiece is frequently used at the end of an articulated arm or fibre-optic cable. This handpiece incorporates a converging lens to focus the laser beam to a precise point a few centimetres from the front of the lens.

For applications in ophthalmology and gynaecology a microscope attachment is more commonly used. This again incorporates a converging lens to focus the laser beam, but also employs a mirror which is finely adjustable in two directions, to direct the beam to its target point.

Laser safety

When using lasers, safety considerations must be paramount for both patient and staff because of the generally high powers of surgical laser systems. However, most of the delivery systems employ a short focal length converging lens to focus the beam, thus causing it to diverge rapidly from the focal point. This means that beyond the first few centimetres the energy density of the laser rapidly decreases, and is thus never likely to be high enough to cause tissue damage.

The principal hazard to either the operator or any other staff present in the treatment area is therefore to the eyes, which can focus any stray laser

absorbed and scattered less than the two lasers just described, and thus penetrates deeper into tissue – approximately 2–3 mm – before being absorbed. It has two major uses.

The first is to vaporise tumours in the gastrointestinal tract. An optical fibre is inserted into an endoscope to carry the laser light to the point of delivery. The second use is in ophthalmology, to produce small holes in the lens capsule or the iris to treat certain relatively rare conditions.

Dye lasers are a new and growing application. They can be 'tuned' to a variety of wavelengths, depending on the particular application required, and produced with a variety of power levels. One use of the dye laser is in the removal of birthmarks such as the port wine stain on the face. Here, yellow-orange laser radiation is preferentially absorbed by the stain, with the resultant heat absorption frequently causing the stain to gradually radiation, possibly causing damage. This stray radiation can be caused by misdirection of the beam or by reflection from surfaces in the room in the case of accidental firing of the beam without the patient in the way!

Staff entering such treatment rooms are therefore alerted by the presence of suitable warning signs. They are usually required to wear safety goggles, made of a material which will absorb sufficient quantities of the particular laser radiation so as to avoid any ocular damage. The rooms should also avoid reflecting surfaces where possible. This is sometimes complex to achieve for infrared lasers, where surfaces that are non-reflecting at optical wavelengths can become highly reflecting in infrared.

Ultraviolet radiation

Ultraviolet (UV) radiation has a number of medical applications which will be considered briefly here, even though they may not be strictly 'optical' in nature.

The UV part of the electromagnetic spectrum is commonly divided by wavelength into three broad areas:

UV-A (near UV) 400–315 nm
UV-B   315–280 nm
UV-C (far UV) 280–100 nm

UV-A radiation damages tissue mainly by thermal effects, whereas UV-B and UV-C radiations mainly cause photochemical reactions to take place. As might be expected, therefore, the three 'bands' produce a range of different effects on the unshielded skin.

The most common reactions are erythema (reddening, or sunburn) and increased melanin production as a protective measure ('tanning'). There is some evidence linking UV-A radiation exposure to skin cancer, although this link is much clearer for UV-B and UV-C radiations. This is because the shorter wavelengths of the UV-B and UV-C radiations are much more effective in producing sunburn and tanning than UV-A radiation. Prolonged UV-A exposure may also lead to premature ageing of the skin and perhaps cataracts in the unprotected eye.

Solar radiation

The most common source of UV radiation is undoubtedly sunlight. Of the broad range of wavelengths emitted by the sun, approximately 5% in energy terms is to be found in the UV part of the spectrum.

The relative quantities of the different UV bands vary considerably with time of day, season, latitude and height above sea level, although UV-A radiation always predominates. At noon on a summer's day in the UK the irradiance (energy per square metre) in the UV-A range will be approximately 40 W m^{-2}, for UV-B approximately 2 W m^{-2}. Levels of UV-C radiation are orders of magnitude smaller.

The principal factor in the large differences between the levels of UV-B radiation reaching the Earth's surface is its absorption by ozone in the atmosphere. The concern regarding the use of aerosol propellent or refrigerant gases such as the chlorofluorocarbons (CFCs) is that they destroy atmospheric ozone, perhaps leading to a future higher level of UV-B radiation over the Earth's surface and hence to a higher level of skin cancer.

Medical uses of UV radiation

The principal medical uses of UV radiation are centred in dermatology (skin diseases) and physiotherapy.

In dermatology, UV radiation is frequently used to treat the chronic skin disease psoriasis, where widespread areas of the body can become affected by patches of rough reddened skin covered with silvery scales. This condition is often treated with a combination of whole-body irradiation by UV-A and a drug which sensitises the skin to UV radiation. The use of the drug means that more UV radiation is absorbed by the affected areas of the skin. This increases the rate of production of new healthy skin cells and hence the effectiveness of the treatment. Another possible therapy uses whole-body irradiation by both UV-A and UV-B radiations.

These whole-body irradiators use up to 50 full-length fluorescent UV-A lamps, arranged in a special cabinet to provide approximately uniform irradiation of the entire body surface. Irradiances at the skin surface of 50–100 W m^{-2} can be achieved in these cabinets.

The output of these lamps, as seen in Figure 6.10(a), has a continuous spectrum in the range 315–400 nm, accompanied by a line spectrum from the mercury in the lamps.

This line spectrum in the UV-A and visible bands gives the lamp a bluish-white appearance in operation, though this plays no part in the treatment's effectiveness. The same type of lamp can also be used in cosmetic (sun-bed) applications, although the irradiance levels may be lower. The output from a UV-B lamp is shown in Figure 6.10(b) for comparison. It may be seen that this lamp produces a much greater output at the lower wavelengths.

Some conditions can increase the skin's sensitivity to UV radiation, and in a few hospitals people can be tested for this hyper-sensitivity. This application uses a device known as a **photo-irradiator**. The source of radiation is a xenon arc lamp, which emits light virtually as a continuous spectrum,

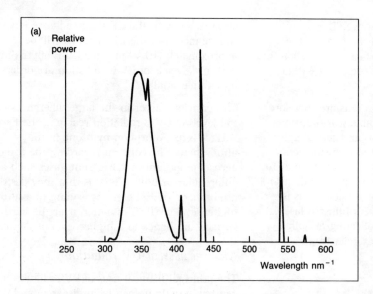

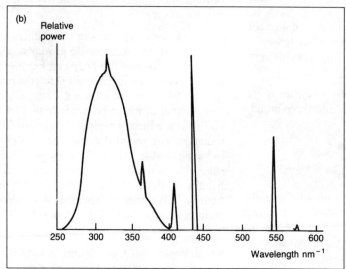

covering approximately the same range as the sun's radiation. The output from the lamp is passed through a monochromator which allows the operator to select a narrow band of wavelengths. This band of wavelengths is passed through a short fibre-optic cable to an applicator.

A range of different wavelengths is then applied to small areas of the skin surface in increasing magnitudes. The skin reactions are then noted to determine at which wavelengths the sensitivity occurs. The particular sensitivity gives the dermatologist a good pointer to the patient's condition, and the appropriate treatment can therefore be given.

Another application of UV radiation is the treatment of conditions such as acne or superficial ulcers. These treatments, for mainly historical reasons, are often done in physiotherapy departments. The source of radiation used is typically a medium-pressure mercury arc lamp, mounted within a reflector to provide a reasonably uniform output light source for general or topical uses. The spectrum of this type of lamp can also be seen in Figure 6.10(c). It may be seen that there is a significant amount of output within the UV-C range. Care must therefore be taken to use a material for the casing of the lamp which will absorb this UV-C radiation. The only exception to this is in the treatment of superficial ulcers, where the bactericidal properties of the UV-C radiation are paramount.

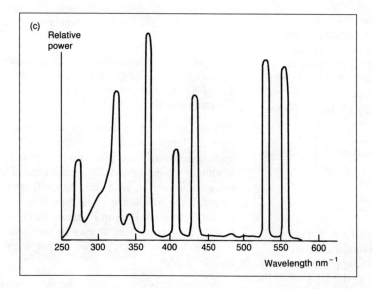

Figure 6.10
(a) Fluorescent UV-A lamp spectrum
(b) Fluorescent UV-B lamp spectrum
(c) Medium-pressure mercury arc lamp spectrum

7 RADIATION UNITS

Background

The definitions and explanations of the terms used concerning ionising radiation are complex, because there are a number of terms which on first glance appear almost identical yet are in reality very different.

The situation is not helped by the fact that in the very recent past the long-standing definitions and units were replaced by SI units which are only slowly being accepted and used both nationally and internationally. Much of the literature and many people still use the old units. For these reasons a conversion table between the old and the new units has been included at the end of this chapter.

Despite all this, however, the importance of understanding the differences between the terms cannot be underestimated. There is widespread confusion in the public domain, which results in many terms being used interchangeably and therefore frequently erroneously.

Energy

In common with much nuclear physics terminology, most energies of photons or particles will be given in terms of **electron-volts**, where $1\ \text{eV} = 1.6 \times 10^{-19}$ J. In practice, most energies will be in the multiples keV ($\times 10^3$) or MeV ($\times 10^6$).

Radioactivity

All elements have a number of different **isotopes** – atoms with the same atomic number, Z, but with differing nucleon numbers, A. Many of these isotopes have stable atoms, but some, whether naturally occurring or artificially produced, are unstable due to their composition of protons and neutrons. The instability shows itself by the emission of energy in the form of gamma rays or by particle(s) from the nuclei of the atoms, which may result in a change in A and/or Z. This process is known as **radioactive decay**, and the materials which undergo it are known as **radionuclides**.

It is worth noting here that the terms 'radionuclide' and 'radioisotope' are frequently used to mean the same thing. The term 'radionuclide' will be used almost exclusively in this book, and refers to a nucleus of specified A and Z, and in a specified nuclear state (excited or not). The term 'radioisotope' should really only be used in phrases such as 'Chromium has four stable isotopes and three radioisotopes'.

The process of radioactive decay is essentially statistical, in that for an atom of a given radionuclide there is a fixed probability that it will decay within unit time. The number of atoms decaying in any sample depends only on the number of radioactive atoms present and the probability itself, which is characteristic of the radionuclide.

In mathematical terms this can be written:

$$-dN/dt\ \propto N$$

where N is the number of radioactive atoms. The negative sign in the equation indicates that N is decreasing.

And thus:
$$dN/dt\ = -\lambda N$$

where λ is the probability of decay, known as the **decay constant** or **transformation constant**.

Rearranging and integrating:

$$dN/N\ = -\lambda\ dt$$
And thus: $\quad \log_e (N_t/N_o)\ = -\lambda\ t$
Giving: $\quad N_t\ = N_o.e^{-\lambda t}$

The number of atoms in a sample of radioactive material therefore falls exponentially with time, at a rate dependent only on the decay constant, λ.

Activity

The activity A of a radionuclide is simply defined as the number of atoms decaying per unit time.

Thus: $\qquad A\ = dN/dt$

and has units of s^{-1}.

A special unit has been adopted for the measurement of activity, the becquerel (Bq), where:

$$1\ \text{Bq}\ = 1\ \text{s}^{-1}$$

The becquerel is in fact a very small unit, and the multiples kBq ($\times 10^3$) and MBq ($\times 10^6$) are used much more frequently in practice.

Now, as: $\qquad A\ = dN/dt = -\lambda N$
We can rewrite: $\quad N_t\ = N_o.e^{-\lambda t}$
as: $\qquad\qquad A_t\ = A_o.e^{-\lambda t}$

and thus the activity of the radionuclide will follow the same exponential decay as does the number of atoms N. This is especially useful as activity is one of the few measurable properties of the radionuclide.

Half-life

One of the special properties of exponential decay is that the time taken for half the atoms of a given sample of a radionuclide to decay, $T_{\frac{1}{2}}$, is constant, and directly related to the decay constant.

We can derive this directly from the equations just given if we substitute $N_0/2$ for N_t (or $a_0/2$ for a_t) in the equations.

Then: $N_0/2 \;=\; N_0 e^{-\lambda T_{\frac{1}{2}}}$

Or: $e^{-\lambda T_{\frac{1}{2}}} \;=\; 2$

Therefore: $\lambda T_{\frac{1}{2}} \;=\; \log_e 2 = 0.693$

And thus: $T_{\frac{1}{2}} \;=\; 0.693/\lambda$

The quantity $T_{\frac{1}{2}}$ is known as the physical **half-life** of the radionuclide.

If we plot the activity of any given radionuclide as a function of time, we will obtain a curve such as Figure 7.1.

Physical, biological and effective half-life

If a substance is introduced into the body its concentration thereafter usually falls with time as it is excreted, usually in the urine or faeces. This biological fall in concentration is often also exponential in nature. If this hypothetical substance is in fact a radionuclide, its fall in concentration within the body will therefore be faster than is accounted for by its physical radioactive decay alone. We will see an **effective decay constant**, λ_e, which will be a combination of its physical decay constant, λ_p, and a biological decay constant, λ_b.

Thus: $\lambda_e \;=\; \lambda_p + \lambda_b$

But since the decay constant $\lambda = 0.693/T_{\frac{1}{2}}$, the above equation can be rewritten:

$$1/T_{\frac{1}{2}e} \;=\; 1/T_{\frac{1}{2}p} + 1/T_{\frac{1}{2}b}$$

where $T_{\frac{1}{2}e}$, $T_{\frac{1}{2}p}$ and $T_{\frac{1}{2}b}$ are the effective, physical and biological half-lives respectively.

For example, chromium-51 (physical half-life 28 days) is used to measure the red blood cell volume and survival times. In the normal patient, the biological half-life of a mixed cell population is approximately 32 days, and so the effective half-life we would actually measure would be:

$$1/T_{\frac{1}{2}e} \;=\; 1/28 + 1/32 \text{ (days)}$$

Or: $T_{\frac{1}{2}e} \;=\; 15$ days

Without a good estimate of the biological half-life, we will of course be unable to do accurate calculations on people who have ingested radioactive materials. Differences in diet or metabolism – the latter frequently being found in disease states – may significantly alter the value of $T_{\frac{1}{2}b}$ and make any calculation extremely difficult. To take the example quoted above, some anaemic conditions can reduce the biological half-life to as little as 3 days!

Until now we have been considering the measurement of the amount of radiation coming *from* a radionuclide. The rest of the chapter will deal with the measurement of the effects of this radiation *on* the medium through which it passes or is absorbed.

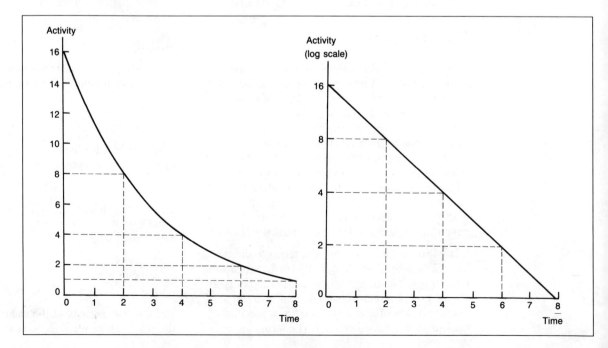

Figure 7.1 Activity versus time for a radionuclide

Exposure

From the early days following the discovery of ionising radiation, one of the principal ways of measuring its effects has been by the amount of ionisation it actually produces.

For over 60 years air has been used as the standard medium for these measurements for two very good reasons. Firstly it is easier to collect the ions produced by radiation in a gaseous substance than in a liquid or solid; and secondly its effective proton number of 7.4 is very close to that of many living tissues (approximately 7.6), with which we are largely concerned when dealing with the effects of ionising radiation.

The actual definition of exposure has undergone a number of changes over the years, and currently says that exposure, X, is the absolute value of the total charge, Q, of the ions of one sign produced in air when all the electrons and positrons liberated by photons in a mass m of air are completely stopped in air.

Thus: $X = Q/m$

and the unit is C kg^{-1}.

Although the definition is relatively straightforward, it does have practical limitations. These principally stem from the facts that:

(a) it applies only to X- and gamma ray photons
(b) it deals only with ionisation in air, whereas we are clearly more concerned with assessing the damage that may be caused by energy absorption from the radiation in living tissue. For this reason the concept of an absorbed 'dose' of ionising radiation has grown in importance.

Absorbed dose

The absorbed dose, D, is defined as the mean energy, E, imparted by ionising radiation per unit mass m of that material.

Thus: $D = E/m$

and it has units J kg^{-1}.

Because the J kg^{-1} is really a measure of the energy imparted by any process, a special unit called the **gray** (Gy) has been sanctioned for use with the measurement of absorbed dose from ionising radiation.

Absorbed dose is a much more general term than exposure, since it can refer to all types of ionising radiation as well as any material. Its practical measurement is much more difficult, however, and involves complex calorimetry. Because of this absorbed dose is most frequently calculated from a measurement of exposure, as will be seen in later chapters.

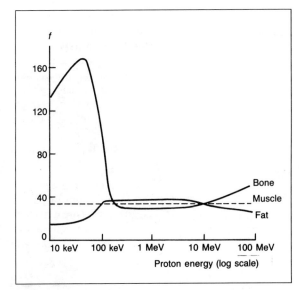

Figure 7.2   Variation of *f* with energy for different tissues

Relationship between absorbed dose and exposure

The relationship between the absorbed dose, D, and exposure, X, is direct for X- and gamma-ray photons, where:

$D = fX$

and as D has the units gray (J kg^{-1}) and X has units of C kg^{-1}, the constant of proportionality f has units of J C^{-1}.

Although the relationship is direct, the value of f in fact varies with both the energy of the X- or gamma-ray photon and the material in which the radiation is being absorbed. This variation is shown graphically in Figure 7.2 for some materials of interest. The actual value of f for air is approximately 34.

At photon energies much above 0.1 MeV the values of f are largely constant and nearly identical for many materials, as at these energies the absorption processes are independent of the proton number Z of the material.

As the energy of the photons falls below 0.1 MeV, however, absorption processes which are more highly dependent on Z predominate, and the values of f vary wildly for the different materials.

The relationship between the absorbed dose and the amount of ionisation produced by other types of radiation follows a similar pattern to that given above for X- and gamma-ray photons. However, a number of other factors are involved depending on the exact methods used in the measurements. These need not concern us here.

Equivalent dose

As we have seen, the measurement of absorbed dose is an important step towards identifying an index of harm following exposure to ionising radiation. It is not, however, the sole determining factor. Different types of radiation have been shown to have markedly different damaging biological effectiveness. Both neutrons and alpha particles, for example, impart energy more densely per unit length of tissue than beta particles or X- and gamma-ray photons – they have a higher **linear energy transfer** or **LET**. This greater density of energy deposition gives an increased likelihood of cell damage and hence biological effect.

These differences in biological effectiveness are taken into account by the so-called **radiation weighting factor**, w_R. The values of w_R for the different types of radiation are kept under review, but are currently as shown in Table 7.1.

Table 7.1

Type of radiation	Radiation weighting factor w_R
beta particles / X- and gamma rays	1
neutrons	5–20
alpha particles	20

The combination of the absorbed dose and the radiation weighting factor produces the **equivalent dose**, H_T, where:

$$H_T = w_R\, D$$

Now as w_R is a dimensionless number, the unit of equivalent dose H_T would be the same as for absorbed dose – the gray (J kg^{-1}). However, to distinguish between the absorbed dose and equivalent dose, the unit of equivalent dose has been given a special name – the **sievert** (Sv).

Effective dose

As we will see in the next chapter, different body tissues show very different sensitivities to ionising radiation. Because of this, the International Commission on Radiological Protection (ICRP) proposed a set of weighting factors to modify the equivalent dose. These factors have undergone recent revision, and are given in Table 7.2.

Table 7.2

Organ	Weighting factor
testes and ovaries	0.20
stomach	0.12
colon	0.12
red bone marrow	0.12
lung	0.12
thyroid	0.05
female breast	0.05
liver	0.05
oesophagus	0.05
bladder	0.05
remainder*	0.05
bone surfaces	0.01
skin	0.01

(*The remainder of the effective dose is the average dose to the rest of the body.)

If only a part of the body is exposed to ionising radiation, the equivalent doses to the organ or organs exposed are multiplied by their weighting factors and added together. In this way a single figure for the radiation dose is produced to represent the dose that, if it were applied uniformly to the whole body, would produce the same biological effect. This figure is called the **effective dose**.

Thus:
Effective dose $H_e = w_1 H_1 + w_2 H_2 + \ldots + w_n H_n$

Where:
w_n = weighting factor of that organ and
H_n = equivalent dose to that organ

The unit of effective dose is also the sievert (Sv).

As an example, we may wish to calculate the effective dose to a patient who has had a lumbar spine X-ray examination. Typically this patient may have received the following doses:

Ovaries:	3.46 mSv
Red bone marrow:	1.41 mSv
Bone surfaces:	1.56 mSv
Other organs:	4.47 mSv

The effective dose for this examination would be:

$$
\begin{aligned}
H_e &= (3.46 \times 0.2) + (1.41 \times 0.12) + \\
&\quad (1.56 \times 0.01) + (4.47 \times 0.05) \\
&= 0.69 + 0.17 + 0.02 + 0.22 \\
&= 1.10 \text{ mSv}
\end{aligned}
$$

When radiation doses in the scientific and other media are given in sieverts, care must be taken in interpreting these figures, as they may in fact be equivalent doses *or* effective doses. As we have just seen, the difference may be very significant! On occasions when doses are given in the old units, even more confusion can arise, as rads are often misused when rems are the appropriate unit (see below).

Old and new units

Table 7.3 gives conversions between old and new radiation units.

Table 7.3

Quantity	New unit	Old unit	Conversion
activity	Bq	Curie (Ci)	1 Bq = 2.7 × 10^{-11} Ci
			1 Ci = 3.7 × 10^{10} Bq
exposure	C kg^{-1}	Roentgen (R)	1 C kg^{-1} = 3876 R
			1 R = 2.58 × 10^{-4} C kg^{-1}
absorbed dose	Gy	rad	1 Gy = 100 rad
			1 rad = 10^{-2} Gy
equivalent dose/ effective dose	Sv	rem	1 Sv = 100 rem
			1 rem = 10^{-2} Sv

Table 7.4 summarises current radiation units and their meanings.

Table 7.4

Quantity	Symbol	Unit	Description
exposure	X	C kg^{-1}	charge produced per unit mass of air
absorbed dose	D	Gy	absorbed energy per unit mass of material
equivalent dose	H_T	Sv	dose × radiation weighting factor (depends on relative biological effectiveness of the radiation)
effective dose	H_e	Sv	sum of (equivalent dose × organ weighting factors) (depends on relative radio-sensitivities of different body tissues)

Questions

1. Explain what is meant by **equivalent dose** and why it is important in radiation dosimetry. Calculate the energy delivered to a person of mass 70 kg by an equivalent dose to the whole body of 30 mSv (3 rem), half being acquired from radiation of weighting factor one, the remainder from radiation of weighting factor three.

2. a) Define the unit of radiation exposure. Describe the mode of action of an ionisation chamber and explain how it is used to measure exposure.

   b) Define the unit of absorbed dose and calculate the absorbed dose in air when the exposure is one unit.

   c) A neutron beam and a beam of gamma rays each produce the same absorbed dose in a certain body. State whether the equivalent doses are the same and give a reason for your answer.

   The charge on an electron = -1.6×10^{-19} C
   Energy required to produce one ion pair in air = 34 eV

8   THE BIOLOGICAL EFFECTS OF RADIATION

Radiation and the cell

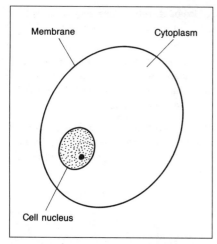

Figure 8.1   Simple representation of a cell

From a simplistic point of view the cell has three basic components, as can be seen in Figure 8.1.

There is the **membrane** which encloses the cell; the **cytoplasm**, which is composed mainly of water; and the **cell nucleus** which contains **DNA**. DNA is a complex molecule which carries all the information necessary to synthesise the different body proteins which affect the genetic characteristics of the organism.

The process of cell division is called **mitosis**, and in most cases occurs when the DNA in the cell nucleus reproduces itself and splits into two. In most organisms (including humans) the process of cell growth is carefully controlled, and in an adult it just keeps pace with the number of cells lost through degenerative or other processes.

Radiation affects the cell by causing ionisation of its molecules. If this ionisation causes damage to the molecules comprising the cell membrane the exact effect on the cell is uncertain, as it may affect the permeability of the cell causing a redistribution of the molecules and ions within the cell itself.

If the ionisation process affects the cytoplasm, molecular fragments known as free radicals may be produced in the cell water. These electrically neutral H• and OH• fragments are highly reactive and may go on to form gaseous hydrogen or hydrogen peroxide, which in turn can damage the DNA in the cell nucleus.

If the radiation makes a direct 'hit' on the cell nucleus, the DNA may be damaged and the chemical form of its complex molecule changed. If the DNA code is changed even in a subtle way, the proteins synthesised by the cell and its pattern of growth will change. This process is known as **mutation**, and may in some instances cause the changed cell to grow uncontrollably, as in cancer. It may also cause the inability of the cell to undergo further mitosis and therefore lead to cell death.

At low doses of radiation, the damage may be limited to a very few cells, and as we have seen there will be a variety of possible effects on the organism. This pattern of damage or effect is known as **stochastic**, meaning random.

At higher doses of radiation, more cells are likely to be 'hit' on multiple occasions, with a resultant increase in the chance of cells being sterilised or destroyed. This means that instead of the normal replacement of cells in the area(s) irradiated, the affected cells will not be replaced and a more sustained pattern of damage will occur. This type of effect is known as **non-stochastic**, as it is non-random, or more predictable.

Stochastic effects

Stochastic effects are usually subdivided into two classes. The first of these are known as **somatic** effects, and occur in the individual exposed to the radiation. The second class are called **genetic** effects, and occur in future generations. It should be noted, however, that almost all stochastic effects are based on cell mutation from DNA damage and hence are really 'genetic' in origin.

The predominating stochastic effect is undoubtedly that of cancer induction in the individual exposed, though the latency period – the time between exposure and the production of the cancer – is often extremely variable. For this reason it has been suggested that other 'triggers' may be necessary to promote the growth of the cancer, such as chemical agents, tobacco smoke or viral infections.

There is little data regarding the dose levels at which these effects occur. The subject is a contentious one, and will be dealt with more fully under the heading 'Risk factors' (page 66).

Non-stochastic effects

Non-stochastic effects will affect different organs (or organisms) at differing radiation dose levels, but in general each effect appears to have a threshold dose below which it is not seen. Above this threshold the probability and severity of the effect increases as the radiation dose increases.

Figure 8.2 shows the range of non-stochastic effects and the dose levels at which they most usually occur.

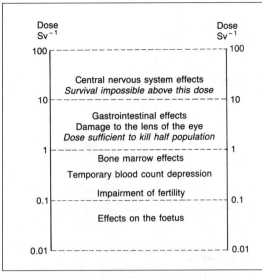

Figure 8.2   Non-stochastic effects and dose levels

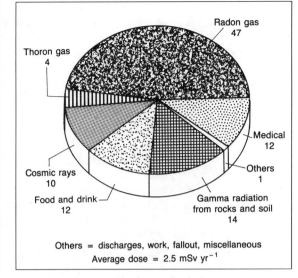

Figure 8.3   Sources of background radiation

It can be seen that perhaps the highest sensitivity to radiation occurs in the foetus. From doses of the order of 0.1 Sv (100 mSv) mental retardation of the foetus and other abnormalities may occur. This is particularly true during the period 4–15 weeks after conception, when there is the greatest development of organs and brain tissue. Doses of 1 Sv may produce foetal death.

As the dose climbs above 0.1 Sv, the next most likely non-stochastic effect is a temporary loss of fertility. This is more likely to affect the testes, and in general terms higher radiation doses nearer to 1 Sv will be required before the ovaries are affected and impairment of fertility occurs in women (because the ovaries are partially 'shielded' within the body).

If the radiation dose reaches approximately 0.5 Sv there is likely to be a temporary depression in the blood count. The severity of and recovery from this effect will clearly depend on the dose received. If it is greater than 2–5 Sv, recovery will not occur and the person will probably die within a few weeks.

If the skin is contaminated by beta-emitting radionuclides, skin burns will occur from around 3 Sv, again worsening in severity as the dose increases.

In the range 3–5 Sv, up to half the total population would be killed, and at these levels both damage to the lens of the eye and gastrointestinal effects would be observed. In the latter case death occurs within days due to the destruction of the gut wall and resultant infections.

Above 10 Sv survival is generally considered to be impossible, and at around 20 Sv death occurs within hours due to central nervous system failure. The exact mechanisms are somewhat uncertain, but are probably due to the collapse of small blood vessels within the brain.

Much of this data also arises from studies on the victims of the atom bombs and from other groups who have been exposed to large doses of radiation.

Background and artificial radiation

Until now we have been considering the effects of specific exposures to doses of ionising radiation, albeit at a variety of different levels, but it should be remembered that we are all continually exposed to a low-level **background** radiation.

This background radiation comes from a group of very different sources, and data from the National Radiological Protection Board (NRPB) suggest that for a typical UK resident their relative contributions are as in Figure 8.3, and amount to about 2.5 mSv yr^{-1}.

It can be seen that something like 87% of the total background radiation dose comes from 'natural' sources. Of these, the largest component is from the gas radon caused by radioactive decay of radium and thorium present in rocks, most notably granite. The actual dose from this source shows considerable geographical variation, and in some parts of the country such as Cornwall and North Derbyshire it may raise this 'background' level to over 20 mSv yr^{-1}.

Other components of the natural background radiation come from gamma rays emitted from radionuclides in the rocks and soil, from cosmic rays which strike the Earth, and from naturally occurring radionuclides in our food, drink and our bodies themselves.

The other 13% of background radiation is a more recent addition to the total, and comes from artificial sources. By far the largest component of this arises from the medical uses of radiation, of which X-rays form the overwhelming majority. The only other noteworthy component is the 0.1% that arises from discharges of radioactive material in the nuclear industry. This obviously has the potential to cause much greater levels of radiation dose (such as after an event like Chernobyl), but under normal working conditions its overall contribution over the whole population is very small.

Risk factors

It would clearly be useful to have an estimate of the likelihood of harm from a given dose of radiation – a **risk factor**. The figures quoted for these risk factors usually relate to the probability of death occurring as a result of the radiation exposure.

The difficulty with calculating such a risk factor is that it depends on how the degree of harm caused by a dose of radiation is related to the level of dose itself. This relationship is formalised in a graph known as a **dose–response curve**.

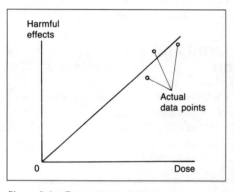

Figure 8.4 Dose–reponse curve

The mainstream view is that the dose–response curve is actually a straight line that passes through the origin, suggesting the harmful effects produced by radiation are directly proportional to the dose received. This is shown in Figure 8.4. Unfortunately a problem arises because the data points where actual effects and reasonably known radiation doses have been measured lie some distance away from the area which would accurately define the 'curve' all the way down to zero effects. However, using the linear model as the basis for most dose–response calculations does mean that it is at least possible to quote an estimate for the risk of damage (such as death, cancer or genetic effects) per sievert of absorbed effective dose.

The current values of the risk factors used by the International Commission on Radiological Protection (ICRP) for assessing the risk of fatal cancer are:

5×10^{-2} Sv^{-1} (population of all ages)
4×10^{-2} Sv^{-1} (population of working age)

These figures are effective doses, and are calculated using risk assessment comparisons. For example:

The IRCP risk factor of 5×10^{-2} Sv^{-1}
means a risk of   5 in 100 Sv^{-1}

or   1 in 20 Sv^{-1}
                    = 1 in 20 000 mSv^{-1}

These risk factors have recently been adjusted upwards by a factor of 4, due to re-calculations of the data from the survivors of the atom bombs on Hiroshima and Nagasaki.

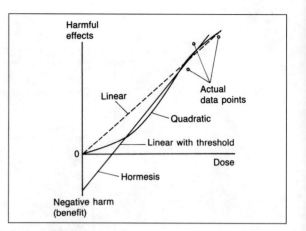

Figure 8.5 Other possible dose–response curves

Much controversy surrounds this whole field, however, as can be seen from the large variety of other possible dose–response curves shown in Figure 8.5. Alongside the linear model we have been discussing, another model has been proposed that also goes through the origin, but is a curve following a **quadratic** form. This model suggests that fewer effects than predicted by the linear model would be seen at low doses, but they would eventually climb to reach the same level of effects near the 'known' area.

Other scientists argue that there is a **threshold** effect – that no effects occur until a certain level of radiation dose is reached. Some would go further and claim that low doses of radiation are actually beneficial – the so-called **hormesis** effect.

The existence of the many dose–effect models indicates the real uncertainty in the actual figures themselves. The very random nature of the effects means that we cannot predict which members of the population will be affected, and indeed the effects may only be observable if the population is very large. Also, as the radiation dose is reduced, its effects will become indistinguishable from other effects causing the same disease processes in the population, and thus will become unmeasurable. Without the exposure of a large population to known doses of radiation, which is hopefully unthinkable, such precise data may never be available.

Legislative framework

We have just shown that it is possible to arrive at an estimated risk factor for the effects of low-level radiation exposure. Using these risk factors it is the task of scientific advisers and legislators to come up with levels that should not be exceeded for the 'safe' use of radiation.

However, if we use the linear model for the dose–response relationship, it is easy to come up with statements such as 'There is *no* safe level of radiation.' While this is certainly consistent with the scientific model, it does nothing to allay anxiety and fear which may in fact be misplaced – for while there may not be a 'safe' level of radiation, there is also no 'safe' way of crossing the road or even of living! There are in fact many activities that we take for granted which can also be shown to follow similar relationships, where the harm that may ensue from an activity is directly related to the level of that activity.

If we are to permit the beneficial uses of radiation, we must therefore balance these advantages against the harm which may result. For this reason, three principles underpin these uses of radiation. The principles are enshrined in the various items of legislation under which radiation is used.

The first is **justification** – that all practices involving radiation need to be justifiable and should produce net benefit.

The second principle, and perhaps the most important, is usually known by its acronym **ALARA** – as low as reasonably achievable. This is fairly self-explanatory, in that it demands that any justifiable radiation exposure must result in the minimum dose consistent with achieving its ends. It is however a principle which is deceptively difficult to keep to in the real-life situation. This will become apparent when X-ray and radionuclide imaging techniques are discussed later (in Chapters 11 and 12).

The third element of this balancing act is the concept of **dose limitation** – that given the first two principles, there are nevertheless absolute limits which should not be reached and should never be exceeded. These are currently:

Classified radiation workers	50 mSv yr^{-1}
Members of the public	5 mSv yr^{-1}

Recent recommendations have suggested that these should be reduced to 20 mSv yr^{-1} and 1 mSv yr^{-1} respectively.

At a public dose limit of 1 mSv yr^{-1} we may compare the risks from ionising radiation with other risks in the public domain, as shown in Table 8.1.

Table 8.1

Cause	Risk of death yr^{-1}
smoking 10 cigarettes/day	1 in 200
natural causes at 40 years old	1 in 850
accident on the road	1 in 9500
radiation at 1 mSv yr^{-1}	1 in 20 000
accident in the home	1 in 26 000

Although the annual dose limit is 1 mSv, the average public dose is in fact much lower. Thus the public risk from ionising radiation appears to compare favourably with other public risks.

Many questions nevertheless remain, such as:

(a) Are the risk factors accurate? The other numbers in the above table are actual values whereas the radiation figures are predictions. What if these risk factors are wrong?

(b) What of the genetic risks? Inclusion of these may significantly raise the risk estimates, especially as the current values are only based on animal data.

(c) Are the risks of high-LET radiation (alpha particles and neutrons, which deposit energy more densely in tissue, see page 62) adequately known? This once again may be the source of significant error.

(d) Can we make this type of comparison? The use of risk–benefit analysis (or more usually cost–benefit analysis) is in itself controversial, based as it is on value judgements such as 'how much is a life worth?'.

In the midst of all these doubts and questions we are still faced with the need to make the best possible decisions as to how we may use ionising radiation. These decisions are not straightforward!

DETECTION AND MEASUREMENT OF RADIATION

Background

This chapter will describe the most important and commonly used methods for detecting ionising radiation.

It is clearly necessary, if only from a safety point of view, to be able to accurately determine both the type of radiation and the quantities present in any given situation. This is not an easy task, since the nature of the radiation can be so variable. For example, it may be heavy particles such as the alpha particle or neutron, or electromagnetic radiation such as the X- or gamma ray. In addition, the range of energies it can possess can vary from a few eV to several MeV (i.e. over a range of at least 10^6). The quantity of radiation present may also vary by at least the same range, from background radiation to that seen in the heart of a nuclear reactor.

No single detector can cope with the extensive range of these requirements. Indeed, detectors which provide an excellent answer to one problem may be totally inappropriate for another.

The detectors described here are subject to gradual development and refinement. Following chapters will show how such developments have allowed us to extend the use to which ionising radiation, once accurately measured, can be put.

Ionisation detectors

The gaseous ionisation process

Detectors of this type are based on the ability of radiation to cause ionisation within a gas-filled chamber. The gas within the chamber is most often air at atmospheric pressure, but inert gases such as argon or xenon are also used. Different detector types may use higher or lower pressures than atmospheric pressure.

The common feature of all such detectors is a pair of electrodes with a high voltage across them to generate an electric field within the chamber. As radiation enters the chamber ionisation occurs, and the electrons and positive ions migrate towards their respective electrodes with a speed that is dependent on the voltage across the chamber. The positive ions, being heavier, will take longer to collect. Once collected, the electrons and ions will induce a charge on the electrodes which can be amplified and counted as an electronic 'pulse'.

Differing effects occur within the chamber depending on the size of the high voltage, but they can be summarised into a number of reasonably discrete regions, as shown in Figure 9.1.

If the electric field is weak (1) the ions drift apart slowly and many of the electrons and ions will recombine before reaching the collecting electrodes. A significant proportion of the ionisation will therefore not be registered, and the size of the electronic pulse produced will be low.

If the voltage across the electrodes is increased, the electrons are rapidly swept towards the anode and recombination is much less likely. At this voltage virtually all of the ions produced within the chamber can be collected. A region is reached (2) known as the **saturation** region, since the chamber is saturated with electrons and ions.

If the voltage is increased beyond this plateau region, the electric field accelerates the electrons produced by the ionising radiation. With this energy the ionised electrons themselves are moving

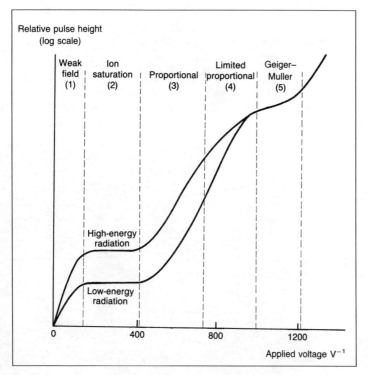

Figure 9.1   Gaseous ionisation effects

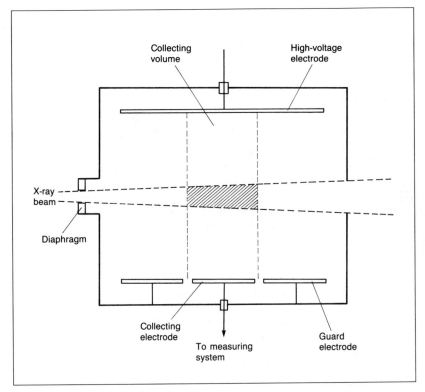

Figure 9.2
The free-air chamber

ions effectively disables the detector from counting any further pulses until they can be collected.

If the voltage across the electrodes is increased beyond the Geiger–Muller region gas discharges will occur. This is spectacular, but not much use for detecting ionising radiation!

Practical ionisation detectors – saturation region

The most common ionisation detectors are those using the saturation region of the response curve. In this region great accuracy of measurement is possible (errors <0.1%) because all the ionisation produced in the gas can be collected. This type of detector is therefore used whenever precise measurements need to be made, such as in the calibration of machines used in radiation therapy.

The most accurate ionisation detector is undoubtedly the **free-air chamber**, shown diagrammatically in Figure 9.2.

The shielding and opening around the detector allows the entry of radiation only from a fixed direction and area. The unusual electrode arrangement is designed so that the curved lines of electrostatic force near the edges of the electrodes do not contribute to the detected ionisation pulse. The arrangement therefore allows only ions within a fixed, regular volume to be collected. To ensure that no secondary ionisation occurs if high-energy radiation is being measured, the separation of the plates has to be adjusted, and can reach distances of over 1 metre. Thus the free-air chamber is not a readily portable instrument! Its principal use is as a calibration instrument, a standard against which other instruments can be compared.

A more common instrument is the so-called **thimble chamber**. As its name suggests, it uses a chamber of small volume, frequently less than 1 cm³. This enables measurements of exposure or exposure rate (number of ionisations per unit mass of air per second) to be made at a well-defined point. Typical arrangements are shown in Figure 9.3.

fast enough to cause further ionisation within the chamber. This extra ionisation means that the size of the electronic pulse is larger than in the saturation region. The size of the pulse is in fact approximately proportional to the amount of energy deposited in the chamber, and this region (3) is known as the **proportional** region. The response time of the detector is slower in this region than in the saturation region because of the additional time needed to collect the extra ions.

If the voltage is increased still further, a second plateau is reached (4) – the **Geiger–Muller** region. Here the electric field is strong enough to produce multiple secondary ionisations which cause an avalanche, overwhelming the gas in the detector. Although the electrons reach the anode fairly quickly, the large number of slower-moving positive

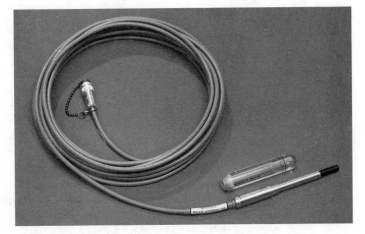

Figure 9.3   Thimble chamber and circuit

Here the air is enclosed within a chamber whose walls are made of material which has a similar effective atomic number and electron density as air. Such material is known as air-equivalent, with graphite being a popular example. The wall must be thick enough to stop the entry of charged ions from outside the chamber, but thin enough to allow radiation to pass inside. The inner surface of the wall is made electrically conducting, to be used as one electrode. The other electrode is a thin wire running down the centre of the chamber, insulated from the wall.

Such a chamber can be used in two modes. In the first the charge collected is accumulated, using a capacitor, to give a measurement of exposure. The second mode uses the charge to develop a voltage across a large resistor. This voltage will change in proportion to the change in the charge collected, and can therefore be used to measure exposure rate.

The thimble chamber is used extensively in practice, for example for measuring outputs from X-ray sets. Its accuracy is good over a wide range of energies, although at both very low and very high energies this accuracy falls off somewhat. For this reason, corrections must be made for the chamber's varying response to energy. The magnitudes of these corrections are found when it is calibrated against a standard instrument.

It should be noted that for any unsealed chambers used at atmospheric pressure, corrections also have to be made for both temperature and pressure, since they will both affect the mass of air present within the chamber volume (exposure = charge per unit mass of air, see page 61). For a chamber calibrated at 760 mm Hg and 293 K, the reading taken at a pressure P mm Hg and temperature t °C will need the following correction:

$$\text{Corrected reading} = \text{meter reading} \times [760/P] \times [(t+273)/293]$$

Proportional ionisation detectors

Ionisation detectors based on the proportional region of the pulse height–voltage curve use the larger pulse produced to give detectors of high sensitivity. The larger pulse also permits the use of less complex amplification circuitry, giving this type of detector a role as a field instrument. A variety of gases are used in these detectors, depending on the type of radiation to be counted, with xenon, butane or boron trifluoride being common.

Because of their sensitivity, these detectors have found particular use for measuring radioactive contamination of surfaces. This type of application commonly uses detectors of area 200–300 cm^2, which can be swept close to the surface to be monitored.

The proportional detector provides a limited ability for discriminating between the different types of radiation based on their differing ionisations. This property makes the detector useful in areas where mixed sources of radiation may be found. Many of these properties are shared with the scintillation detector described below.

Geiger–Muller detectors

In the relatively large electric field of the Geiger–Muller detector, the pulses produced are the same size regardless of the type or energy of the triggering radiation because of the avalanche ionisation that takes place within the gas. This type of detector therefore functions as a pure pulse counter.

Geiger–Muller detectors have found widespread use as survey instruments for detecting low levels of radiation, as they are very sensitive and require only simple amplification. However, the very avalanche effect which produces such a large pulse means that the detector can be easily disabled by relatively low count rates, as no further ionising radiation can be detected while the avalanche effect is in progress. For this reason an additional 'quenching' gas such as chlorine, bromine or ethanol is added to the gas in the chamber. This quenching gas can absorb the positive ions and allow the chamber to count further pulses more quickly.

Geiger–Muller detectors come in wide variety of shapes and sizes. They usually consist of a cylindrical glass envelope containing gas at low pressure and a thin central anode wire surrounded by a cylindrical cathode. For counting low-energy or densely ionising radiation the cylinder is usually shorter and of greater diameter, with a thin end window to allow the radiation to enter the detector.

Scintillation counters

Scintillation materials

The scintillation process is basically one of fluorescence, where there is rapid emission of visible radiation from a substance following its excitation. The excitation is caused by the substance absorbing energy, in this case from ionising radiation.

Substances in which scintillation occurs – known as **scintillators** – come in two main types, organic scintillators and inorganic scintillators.

In organic scintillators the fluorescence process arises from changes in the energy levels of a single molecule, and because of this it can be observed whatever the physical state of that molecule. Materials such as anthracene or napthalene will therefore fluoresce whether they are in a solid state, a vapour, or part of a multi-component solution.

With the simple addition of a suitable fluorescent material many plastics can be used as scintillators, and have the advantage that they can then be bent or moulded into the most useful shapes for a particular purpose. Liquid 'cocktails' composed of solutions of mixed scintillators in strong solvents are used to assay beta-emitting radionuclides in a variety of biological materials.

Inorganic scintillators are in the main solid crystalline materials. The most common inorganic scintillators are based on alkali halide crystals, but without the presence of certain impurities they would be virtually useless! These impurities, called **activators**, are routinely added in small quantities to almost all the inorganic scintillators. Their presence greatly enhances the emission of visible light during the fluorescence process by adding special energy levels within the crystal lattice structure.

The principal inorganic scintillator is undoubtedly the sodium iodide crystal with thallium as the activator, often abbreviated to its chemical symbols, NaI(Tl). Caesium iodide with either thallium or sodium as the activator is also used.

The ideal scintillator versus sodium iodide (thallium)

There are a number of properties that go into making the ideal scintillator. As usual, no one substance actually combines all these ideals, but some are better than others.

These properties are explored in Table 9.1.

The photomultiplier tube

The next step in the practical use of any scintillator, whether organic or inorganic, is to collect the scintillations and record them. This is most efficiently done using the so-called **photomultiplier tube**.

The photomultiplier tube (usually known as a PM-tube) is a device which converts the scintillation event into a pulse of electrons. As may be guessed from its name, the PM-tube multiplies this pulse in size so that it may be detected electronically.

The usual arrangement is to optically couple the scintillator to the PM-tube as shown in Figure 9.4.

The scintillations strike a photocathode, a light-sensitive rare-earth material which emits an electron for every 4 or 5 light photons which strike it. The electrons are then accelerated in the evacuated tube by increasingly high voltages towards a series of special electrodes known as dynodes. These are coated in the same rare-earth material as the photocathode.

On impact with each of these dynodes, an electron will cause the emission of 2 or 3 further electrons. Since this happens at each stage, the original electron pulse is amplified by the dynodes in the

Table 9.1	The ideal scintillator	Other scintillators	NaI(Tl)
	The material should convert the kinetic energy of the radiation into detectable light with a high efficiency.	The efficiency varies by a factor of more than 20 between commercially available scintillators.	Sodium iodide has the highest efficiency of any scintillator.
	The conversion should be linear, in that the light yield should be proportional to the energy deposited in the scintillator over a wide range.	This property is achieved well in many scintillators.	This proportionality also holds for sodium iodide.
	The medium should be transparent to its own light emissions.	Some scintillators reabsorb a significant proportion of their own light ouput. This clearly reduces their overall efficiency and is an obvious drawback in the material.	Self-absorption is not a problem for sodium iodide.
	The fluorescence process should be rapid, and the light 'pulse' emitted should decay away rapidly to allow accurate counting of high incident numbers of photons or particles.	This pulse decay time can vary by a factor of 200 or more between scintillators.	For sodium iodide the decay time is 230 ns (2.3×10^{-7} s), which in reality is rather long for fast counting operations.
	The material should be workable into a variety of shapes and sizes.	This property is achieved with a wide range of success for different scintillators, being rather more successful for the organic scintillators than for the inorganics.	Sodium iodide crystals can be grown in a variety of shapes and sizes, but they are hygroscopic, which means they must be hermetically sealed after growth, and are fragile, being susceptible to mechanical and thermal shock.

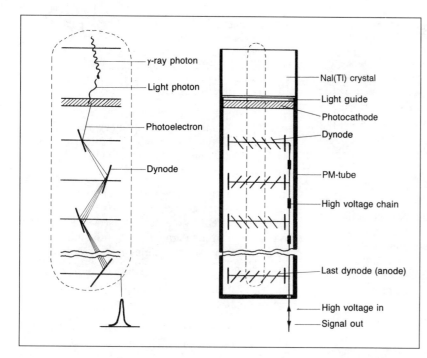

Figure 9.4
A photomultiplier tube

PM-tube to give an overall gain of approximately 10^6. On average a PM-tube will contain 10–12 dynodes, with an anode–cathode voltage between 700 V and 1200 V distributed evenly along the dynode chain by a resistor network.

Since the original scintillator gives out light photons in proportion to the energy deposited in it, and because the amplification factor of the PM-tube is approximately constant, the size of the output electronic pulse of the PM-tube will also be in proportion to the energy deposited by the ionising radiation in the scintillator.

Associated electronic circuitry

The electronic circuitry associated with scintillation detectors is shown diagrammatically in Figure 9.5.

The electronic pulse is initially boosted by a preamplifier to give an output of a few millivolts. The PM-tube and preamplifier are usually constructed as an independent unit.

The pulse is further amplified by a factor of approximately 1000 in a separate unit to give a final output pulse of the order of 1–10 V. This amplifier must be both linear and extremely stable

to maintain the linearity between the deposited energy in the scintillator and the final electronic pulse height.

The pulses are then processed by a circuit known as a pulse-height analyser. This circuit allows the operator to 'count' only those pulses that are of a chosen height range – that is only those pulses originating from a given range of energies.

This range of accepted pulse heights is often referred to as the counting 'window'. Since emitted gamma-ray energies are characteristic of the radionuclide of origin, the pulse-height analyser allows the operator to discriminate between gamma rays from one radionuclide to the exclusion of other radionuclides or background radiation.

Scalar/timers can be added to the circuitry to count the number of pulses within the chosen window. This allows either the time for a given number of pulses, or the count rate (pulses per unit time), to be measured.

Ratemeters can also be added to provide a continuous display of the count rate from a detector. This enables the operator to observe any rapid fluctuations in the count rate.

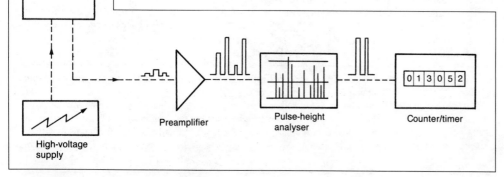

Figure 9.5 Scintillation detector circuit

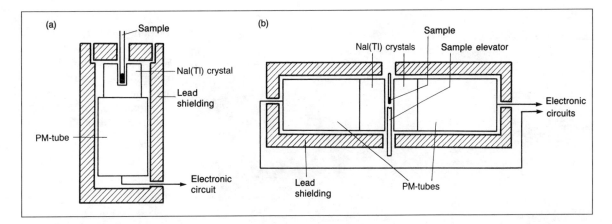

Figure 9.6
(a) Well type and
(b) radial-hole type
scintillation detectors

Practical scintillation detectors

Scintillation detectors, particularly those using NaI(Tl), are used in a variety of situations in the clinical context.

For counting small levels of activity in blood or other samples, the detectors must be designed to maximise the number of detected photons. This is done by surrounding as much of the sample as possible with the scintillator. Such detector systems come in two basic shapes, either the well type or the radial-hole type, as shown in Figure 9.6.

The common feature of both designs is the provision of lead shielding around the scintillation crystal and PM-tube. This cuts down the amount of background radiation reaching the detector, and so improves the sensitivity and accuracy of the count.

The well-type crystal is used in cases where individual samples are to be counted. Following each sample's count, the sample is removed and the next is placed manually into the well.

More often now the radial-hole arrangement is used in so-called automatic sample counters. In this type of counter the samples are lifted into the centre of the hole in the crystal using an elevator system. After counting, the elevator returns the sample to a tray and automatically moves another into the correct position for counting.

The advantage of such counters is that they can be set up to count a large number of samples sequentially. With the aid of microprocessor controls the operator is able to count for different radionuclides and lengths of time per sample.

Automatic sample counters of a slightly different design are also used in liquid scintillation counting. In this application the scintillator is added to the sample as a liquid 'cocktail'. What is required of the counter is to count the scintillations from the liquid, and hence an elevator system raises the sample into the space between two opposed PM-tubes for the scintillations to be counted.

Because of this arrangement care must be taken for the counter to be light tight. Account must also be taken of background scintillations arising from phosphorescence due to chemical reactions while the sample was being prepared or exposed to the light. Any variations in light transmission in the sample will also affect the number of scintillations counted, and so care must be taken in the preparation of the samples to ensure that this variation is kept to a minimum.

For the counting of external sources, such as the levels of iodine-131 in the thyroid gland, NaI(Tl) crystal detectors are again used, this time fitted with a lead collar known as a **collimator**. The purpose of the collimator is to allow only those gamma rays from a defined angle to strike the crystal and be counted. It therefore gives the detector directionality of response.

Such collimated detectors come in a variety of designs, depending upon their use. Some examples are given in Figure 9.7.

Scintillation detectors based on NaI(Tl) crystals are also used in both the rectilinear scanner and the gamma camera – these radionuclide imaging devices are described in Chapter 12.

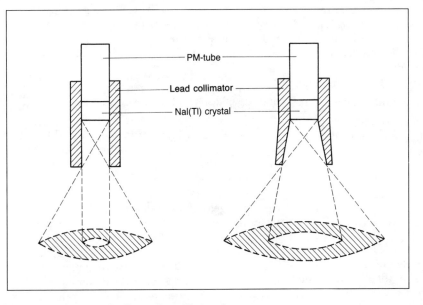

Figure 9.7   Designs of collimated scintillation detectors

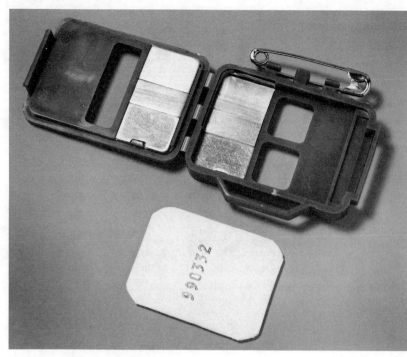

Figure 9.8   A film-badge dosimeter

Film

The use of film to detect the presence of ionising radiation goes back to Henri Becquerel and the discovery of radiation itself. In its use for X-ray imaging, it is also one of the better-known methods, although that particular application of the technique will be discussed in greater detail in Chapter 11.

The basic method of operation is quite straightforward, in that the radiation ionises the silver halide crystals in the film emulsion. This process of ionisation causes a chemical reduction reaction in the crystal, which when developed, blackens that part of the film emulsion. The greater the amount of exposure to ionising radiation, the greater the degree of film blackening.

This method of detecting ionising radiation has long been used as a way of estimating the absorbed dose received by radiation workers. This is the so-called **film-badge dosimeter**, which has a small packet of film with a high concentration of silver halide crystals in a thick emulsion wrapped in a light-tight coating.

In practice, a batch of films is prepared by the monitoring laboratory. Most of the films are sent to the departments where the workers need to be monitored, but

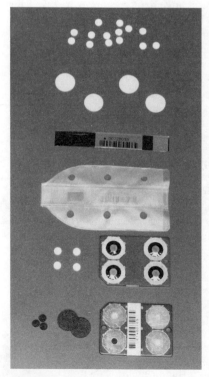

Figure 9.9
Thermoluminescent dosimeters

some are kept back. These films are exposed to known radiation doses from a number of different types of ionising radiation. When all the films are returned, the whole batch is developed. The radiation dose to the wearers of the dosimeters can then be estimated by comparison of the degree of blackening of the wearers' films with the calibration films.

An example of a typical film-badge dosimeter can be seen in Figure 9.8.

The film holder of the dosimeter in fact plays an important part in the overall measuring process. This is because the sensitivity of film is highly dependent on the energy of the ionising radiation (at least for X- and gamma-ray photons). The holder conventionally contains a number of different filters held in contact with the film, together with a totally unfiltered area. The filters are typically composed of materials such as aluminium, lead and different densities of plastic. They are designed to attenuate or remove different types of radiation.

For example, all types of ionising radiation will blacken the unfiltered part of the film, whereas alpha particles will be stopped by all the filters, and beta particles by the aluminium and plastic. Low-energy X-rays will penetrate all but the thicker lead filters, but even these may be penetrated by high-energy gamma rays.

If the degree of blackening in the different parts of the film is compared, then both the type of radiation causing the exposure and the radiation dose to the wearer can be estimated from the film.

Thermoluminescence

The scintillation materials we have previously discussed emit light after exposure to ionising radiation in the form of prompt fluorescence – the scintillation follows rapidly after the exposure.

There is another class of materials which exhibit a property known as **thermoluminescence**, of which lithium fluoride (LiF) is the most commonly used. This type of crystal has a relatively large number of energy levels in its structure which act as 'traps'. When ionising radiation strikes the material, energy is absorbed and electrons are given enough energy to be lifted into these traps. At room temperature there is not enough thermal energy to get them out of the traps again, but when the material is heated, sufficient thermal energy is supplied to do this. The electrons then rapidly fall back to their normal energy levels, emitting light. The temperature required for this heating process varies significantly for different thermoluminescent materials, being around 250 °C for lithium fluoride.

The number of electrons trapped, and hence the amount of light released upon heating, is directly related to the amount of incident radiation striking the material. By comparing the light signal from a given piece of thermoluminescent material with that from another exposed to a known quantity of radiation, the 'dose' to the material can be calculated. These pieces of material form the basis of the **thermoluminescent dosimeter**, usually abbreviated to its initials TLD. A typical TLD badge is shown in Figure 9.9.

The usual arrangement consists of two or four small discs of LiF. These are placed in a light-tight holder to stop exposure to UV radiation, which could cause a falsely increased reading on the TLD. Above one of the discs is a filter designed to represent the skin. The badge is then worn by a radiation worker for a fixed period of time, before being returned.

The light signal from the TLDs are 'read' in a machine which uses a PM-tube to detect and amplify the light signal, with an integrator to determine its magnitude. Once again, by comparing readings from the TLDs worn by radiation workers with others exposed to known doses of radiation, the workers' doses can be estimated.

TLDs are now used extensively for both personnel and environmental monitoring purposes, and in many instances have taken over the role previously occupied by the film-badge. The reasons for this are explored in Table 9.2.

Table 9.2

Property	Film	TLD
accuracy	photons – fair beta particles – poor	photons – very good beta particles – good
photon energy dependence	high – sensitivity falls off rapidly as energy increases above 50 keV	low – above 50 keV the response is nearly linear, below 50 keV it falls off somewhat
measurement range	0.1 mGy–1 Gy	5 μGy–1 kGy
cost	very low	low – a typical TLD 'chip' costs approximately £2–3
reusabilty	no	yes – up to 50 times
size and shape	fair – different sizes and types of emulsion can be produced	very good – TLDs can be machined and extruded into a variety of pellets, discs, etc.
capability for permanent record-keeping	yes – developed film can be re-read at a later date providing the calibrated-dose film is retained for comparison	no – once read the dose record is lost. However, the curve of light output versus heat (glow-curve) can be stored in a computer and re-examined

Solid state detectors

Solid state detectors using semiconductor materials are essentially a solid version of the gaseous ionisation detector. In this type of detector thin pieces of germanium or silicon have small amounts of an impurity (usually lithium) added to them. When ionising radiation strikes the semiconductor, electrons within it are given energy, making the material slightly more conductive. If a voltage is applied across the material, these electrons move and the resulting current can be detected.

The conversion of ionising radiation to electrical charge is much more efficient in solid state detectors than in scintillation detectors, that is, for each photon absorbed, more electrons are produced per unit of that photon's energy in solid state detectors than in scintillation detectors.

Following appropriate amplification, the signal produced by solid state detectors enables more accurate estimates of the photon energy to be made than is possible from scintillation devices. This is because the higher signal outputs lead to lower uncertainties (less electronic noise) in the energy estimates.

Solid state detectors do however suffer from two major disadvantages:

(a) At room temperatures the signal generated by the detection of ionising radiation is heavily swamped by thermal 'noise' in the semiconductor. The detectors must therefore be cooled, frequently to liquid nitrogen temperatures (–192 °C).

(b) Solid state detectors are difficult and costly to produce in large physical sizes. This limits their applications.

Because of this, their principal use is in the field of spectroscopy – identification of radionuclides from their characteristic gamma-ray emissions.

Questions

1. Describe the physical principles underlying the action of a scintillation detector and photomultiplier, i.e. a scintillation counter.

   Why is a thallium-doped sodium iodide crystal [NaI(Tl)] often used as the scintillator material for the detection of gamma rays?   (ULSEB – part question)

2. a) A film badge used for personal radiation monitoring contains various filters through which radiation must pass before reaching the film. Explain how this helps in making an estimate of the dose equivalent received by the wearer of the badge.

   b) Describe the principle of operation of the thermoluminescent dosimeter. (JMB – part question)

10 IONISING RADIATION IN MEDICINE

Background

This chapter explores some of the many uses of ionising radiation in medicine.

Following its discovery, ionising radiation was very quickly put to work in the medical field, particularly in radiotherapy. However, some of these uses now appear naive in the extreme, if not positively dangerous! For example, soon after its discovery, [226]radium was used extensively in everything from health salts to locally applied creams, although it is now classed as potentially one of the more dangerous radionuclides due to its alpha-particle emissions. This change from panacea to hazard shows the rapid pace of scientific discovery as well as the danger of enthusiasm outpacing knowledge.

We now believe we understand the mechanism of radiation damage much more accurately, and in addition technology has made radiation detectors much more sensitive. These factors have lead in turn to the widespread use of ionising radiation, both from external beams and from internally administered radionuclides. In these applications the levels of radiation are tightly controlled, in an attempt to maximise the benefit arising from the information they provide while minimising the possible effects.

The following sections outline tracer studies using radionuclides, imaging and radiotherapy using both radionuclides and external beams, and the necessary studies in radiation detection and measurement which enable these uses to proceed and develop.

Radionuclide tracer studies

Dilution studies

These types of studies have been used with radionuclides for over 50 years, and provide a relatively simple way of measuring the mass or volume of substances such as blood or water within the body.

The basic method is quite straightforward. A measured quantity of a radionuclide is administered to the patient and is allowed time to mix with the substance under test. A representative sample of that substance is then taken, and its radioactivity measured. The degree of dilution the sample has undergone gives a direct measure of the volume of the substance in the body.

This can be written mathematically, as follows. An activity A of the tracer in a volume v is added to the system under test, which has a volume V. The concentration of the tracer after mixing – the activity per unit volume, s – is given by the formula:

$$s = \frac{A}{(V + v)}$$

In practice, v is much smaller than V, and can be ignored. The formula thus reduces to:

$$s = \frac{A}{V} \quad \text{or} \quad V = \frac{A}{s}$$

And because s is just the activity per unit volume of the tracer,

$$V = \frac{A \, v_s}{s}$$

where v_s is the volume of the sample taken.

This method makes two significant assumptions. The first is that complete mixing has taken place, that is, the concentration of the tracer is constant throughout the substance under test. This assumption is usually, but not always, the case. Secondly, it assumes that the concentration of the tracer is in equilibrium, that is, that none of the tracer is being excreted or otherwise absorbed from the substance. Again this is usually the case providing the tracer has been carefully chosen. It would otherwise have to be allowed for in the calculation.

The calculation does of course require the administered activity, A, to be known. In practice this is achieved by retaining a 'standard' – a known quantity of the same material that is to be administered. However, this material is frequently too active to be counted in a counter capable of counting the diluted patient samples. For this reason the standard itself is frequently diluted by a known proportion before counting.

The dilution method is still in clinical use. Some of the major examples are given in Table 10.1.

One clinical example concerns the measurement of the red cell volume. This measurement can be clinically important, as a number of blood disorders

Table 10.1

Measurement	Tracer	Labelled compound
plasma volume	^{125}iodine	human serum albumin
red cell volume/mass	^{51}chromium	red blood cells
total body water	^{3}hydrogen	tritiated water
total exchangeable sodium	^{24}sodium	
total exchangeable potassium	^{42}potassium	

will affect the red cell volume, either to increase it or decrease it. The tracer used in this study is the patient's own red blood cells that have been labelled with approximately 2 MBq of ^{51}chromium, in the form of the chemical compound sodium chromate. ^{51}Chromium emits gamma rays of energy 322 keV, which is suitable for use in gamma counters. It has a half-life of 27.8 days and therefore is subject to only negligible radioactive decay during the course of the test.

The radioactive compound is added to approximately 10 cm^3 of the patient's red cells, and after gentle mixing is allowed to 'incubate' – stand together – for approximately 30 minutes. During this time the chromate ions diffuse into the red cells where they are reduced to the chromic form and become attached to the haemoglobin.

The cells are then 'washed' in sterile saline to remove any unlabelled ^{51}chromium, which might label plasma proteins and give rise to false levels of blood radioactivity. Before the solution containing the labelled cells is re-injected, some of it is retained to act as a standard. The radioactively labelled red cells are given 10–15 minutes to mix thoroughly with the rest of the patient's circulation, after which time a venous blood sample is taken from the patient. The red cell volume is calculated as follows, using data from an actual study:

Volume injected (v)	=	10 cm^3
Volume of sample (v_s)	=	1 cm^3
Volume of standard	=	1 cm^3
Dilution of standard	=	1 in 100
Count rate of standard	=	55.32 c s^{-1}
Count rate of sample	=	11.45 c s^{-1}
Weight of patient	=	80 kg
Venous haematocrit, H	=	0.586

(this factor, H, is the volume ratio of red cells to whole blood, and must be introduced because the sample we count is whole blood, whereas the standard is made from the red cells only. The actual value of the ratio varies from patient to patient.)

Injected radioactivity = (count rate of standard) × (volume injected) × (standard dilution)
= 55.32 × 10 × 100
= 55 320 cm^3 c s^{-1}

Sample radioactivity = 11.45 / H
= 11.45 / 0.586
= 19.54 c s^{-1}

Using the formula $V = A / s$,

Red cell volume = (injected) / (sample)
= 55 320 / 19.54
= 2831 cm^3 (= 2.83 l)

This is sometimes expressed as the volume per unit mass of the patient:
= 2831/80 (cm^3 kg^{-1})
= 35.4 cm^3 kg^{-1}

The normal range for the red cell volume is 25–35 cm^3 kg^{-1}, and this patient therefore lies on the upper borderline of normal.

Flow studies

The dilution method is in fact just a specific example of a wider method of analysis known as **compartmental analysis**. This treats the passage of radioactive tracers through the body like the flow of a dye through tanks containing water.

The dilution principle above is based on analysis of a single closed compartment, as in Figure 10.1.

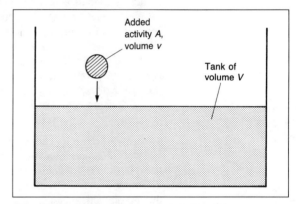

Figure 10.1   Single closed compartment model

If, on the other hand, the compartment is not closed and the 'water' is allowed to escape, as in Figure 10.2 (overleaf), it can be shown that the flow rate F cm^3 s^{-1} is directly proportional to the volume of water in the tank, V cm^3.

Thus: $F = k V$

where k is a constant representing the fraction of the total volume lost per unit time – a rate constant.

This situation is totally analogous to that of radioactive decay, as discussed in Chapter 8, and if the activity of the area is monitored by external counting, an exponential 'decay' curve results.

Using the exponential equation:

$$V = V_o e^{-kt}$$

the rate constant k can be evaluated. Providing the volume of the object under investigation is known to a good approximation, an estimate of the flow can be obtained from the equation:

$$F = k V$$

With an extension of this type of analysis, more

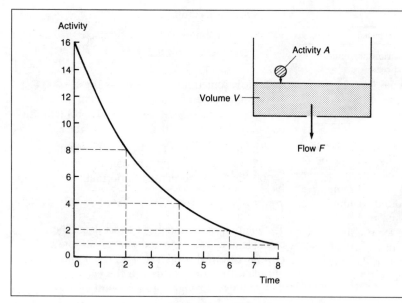
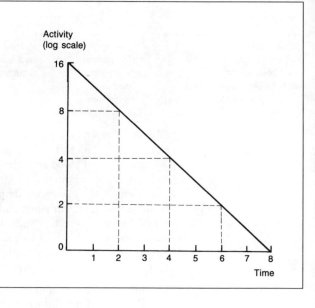

Figure 10.2
Flow/volume in a single open compartment

complex flow systems can be examined. Many clinical examples exist, of which one is the measurement of cerebral blood flow using a solution containing the radioactive inert gas ^{133}xenon, injected intra-arterially. Following such an injection, the exponential fall of the count rate is measured from detectors over different parts of the brain. The rate constants derived from these measurements can then be used to assess the cerebral blood flow in those areas.

Such measurements can be used to assess the extent of damage following, for example, a stroke or in basic physiological studies, for example, in assessing which parts of the brain come into play during different physical and mental tasks.

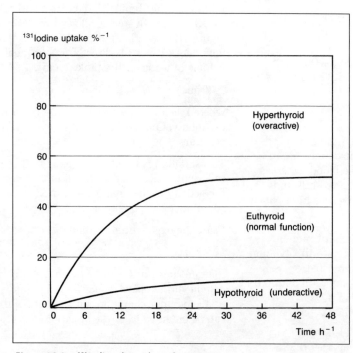

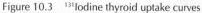
Figure 10.3 ^{131}Iodine thyroid uptake curves

Uptake studies

This type of study uses the degree of uptake of a particular tracer as an assessment of the function of the part of the body under investigation.

The major example of this study is undoubtedly the thyroid uptake study. This uses ^{131}iodine, which emits beta particles and gamma rays of energy 364 keV, the gamma rays enabling its presence to be detected outside the body. It has a half-life of 8.04 days.

It is administered orally as a solution of sodium iodide, in an activity of the order of 0.5 MBq. An equal activity is retained as a reference standard. The counting is done using a scintillation detector with a diverging collimator.

The reference standard is counted in a perspex neck 'phantom', designed to simulate the attenuation and scattering properties of the patient. After allowing for background counts arising from any circulating ^{131}iodine within the patient and from natural background radiation, the uptake of the radioiodine is assessed at fixed times after the administration – usually 4, 24 and 48 hours. The percentage uptake is then given by:

$$\% \text{ uptake} = \frac{\text{counts in thyroid}}{\text{counts in standard}} \times 100$$

The form of the uptake 'curve' is shown in Figure 10.3 for normal, under- and overactive thyroid glands.

Another example of the tracer method, iron kinetic studies, uses both clearance and uptake measurements. This requires an intravenous injection of approximately 200 kBq ^{59}Fe, administered as the compound ferric citrate. Following its injection, the radioactive iron mixes with non-active iron in the blood plasma, and the rate of its uptake into the bone marrow can be assessed by taking a series of blood samples over a period of approximately 2 hours.

Over the next 10 days or so, the radioactive iron will gradually reappear in the circulation in the newly formed red blood cells. By counting the degree of activity in samples of those red blood cells, the percentage of the injected iron incorporated into the cells can be estimated.

This can be combined with external counting measurements over organs such as the liver, spleen, heart and bone marrow. Such measurements follow the fate of red cells in patients with certain types of anaemia, and give an estimation of where and how quickly the red cells are being destroyed. An example from a clinical study is shown in Figure 10.4.

Imaging

Imaging using ionising radiation may be done in two very different ways. The first is essentially an extension of the tracer study just described. The technique again uses the administration of a radionuclide in a suitable chemical form, but instead of merely counting the amount of uptake of the tracer at a given point in time, the distribution of the tracer is examined using a position-sensitive detector. The sophistication of such devices has grown considerably from humble beginnings, and **radionuclide imaging**, or nuclear medicine as it is sometimes known, now plays a significant role in the diagnostic armoury of the modern hospital. The importance of these techniques merits a fuller description, and this is done in Chapter 12.

The second of the two methods of imaging essentially uses differences in the transmission of an external beam of X-radiation to produce a kind of 'shadow image' of the tissue through which it passes. This so-called 'X-ray' is perhaps the most widely known medical diagnostic test. The simplistic description above is in no way adequate for these techniques, which have also undergone considerable development. They will be discussed further in Chapter 11.

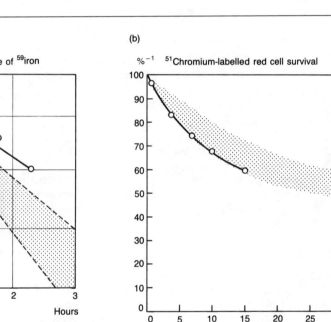

Figure 10.4 A ^{59}iron- and ^{51}chromium-labelled red cell study in a patient with a type of anaemia, where the bone marrow does not produce red blood cells. The curves show a normal (though rapid) removal of ^{59}iron (a) and ^{51}chromium (b) from the blood, but only minimal incorporation of the radioactive iron into the red blood cells (c). A high liver uptake of the labelled red cells (d) shows that the cells do not survive.

Radiotherapy

The technique of radiotherapy uses the very property of ionising radiation that the other techniques strive to avoid – that in sufficient doses it can kill the cells through which it passes. It is used principally in the treatment of cancer, with one or two exceptions that will be described later in this section.

Ionising radiation kills cells indiscriminately, and so for the treatment to be effective more of the cancer cells must be killed than the normal cells around the tumour or tumours within the body. This task is made a little easier since cancer cells are sometimes more sensitive to radiation than normal cells. However, this relative increase in radiosensitivity varies greatly from one type of cell to another, so different doses of radiation are required to kill different types of cancers.

The use of radiotherapy will nevertheless kill a number of the normal tissue cells, especially those in the vicinity of the tumour. Since high doses of radiation are frequently required to destroy the tumour, steps must to be taken to limit the damage to the normal tissue. This is often achieved using a method known as **fractionation**, where the necessary dose of radiation is split into a number of smaller fractions, given over a period of time. This allows the normal tissues time to partially recover between the treatments, and increases the ability of the patient to tolerate the therapy.

There are two main types of radiotherapy, differing by the way the ionising radiation is applied. They are called **teletherapy** and **brachytherapy**.

Teletherapy

Teletherapy is radiotherapy using external beams of radiation. A number of different types of ionising radiation are used in teletherapy. High-energy electrons, protons and mesons produced in particle accelerators are sometimes used. However, the most frequently used type uses electromagnetic radiation – X- and gamma rays.

This radiation is produced in two ways. The first uses a radioactive source of high activity, typically ^{60}cobalt of approximately 300 TB (3×10^{14} Bq). ^{60}Co is used because it emits relatively high-energy gamma rays of 1.17 and 1.33 MeV, and has a half-life of 5.3 years which means that the source does not need to be changed very often. Such a source must of course be heavily shielded, as it will produce external dose rates of the order of 1–2 Gy min^{-1}. (The dose rate is the rate at which the dose is accrued by the patient.)

For these reasons there need to be accurate controls on the specific direction and area in which the radiation is emitted, and accurately measured exposure times. As the source is emitting its radiation continuously, careful shuttering mechanisms need to be employed for these purposes.

The second method uses an X-ray beam, produced by accelerating electrons in a linear accelerator to energies of several MeV, and then forcing them to hit a metal target.

The choice of whether to use a gamma-ray, X-ray or other source of radiation for a particular therapeutic application is a complex one in which a number of variables play a role. Whatever the type of radiation used, high-energy radiation is generally favoured in teletherapy as it is able to penetrate deep into the body more easily than lower-energy radiation.

This can be illustrated using a diagram known as an **isodose chart**, as shown in Figure 10.5. The isodose chart plots the lines of equal dose that would be expected inside the body of the patient, and is similar to the contour lines on a map.

The diagram shows how the isodose lines vary depending on the energy and type of radiation. The increased usefulness of high-energy radiation in

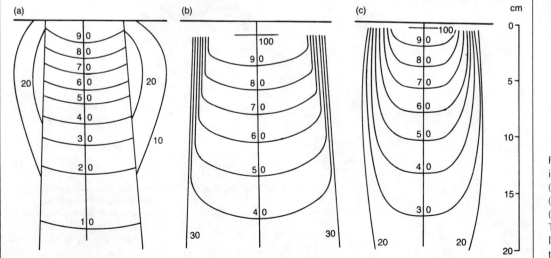

Figure 10.5   Radiotherapy isodose lines for
(a) 250 kVp X-rays
(b) 4 MV X-rays
(c) ^{60}Co gamma rays
The numbers on the contour lines represent the percentage of the maximum dose at any point

80   Medical Physics for Advanced Level

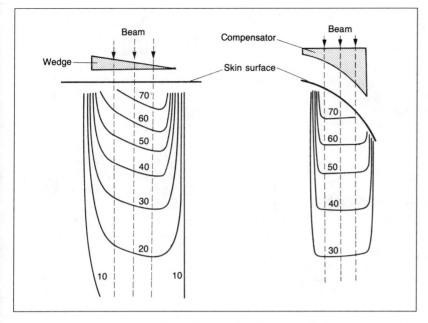

Figure 10.6
The effect of a wedge
and compensator on
an isodose chart

Figure 10.7
Treatment plan

providing dose at depth can easily be seen. The skin surface is not completely flat, however, and some tissues within the body absorb the radiation better than others. For this reason, the 'shape' of the radiation field can be altered using devices known as **wedges** and **compensators**. The effects of these are shown in Figure 10.6.

They alter the field shape because they are not of uniform thickness, and thus more radiation is

absorbed where the wedge or compensator is thicker. Even allowing for this modification of the field shape, if all the dose were to be administered at one point in the body, the skin and any underlying tissues at that entrance point would be very badly affected. For this reason, a number of radiation fields are used. These somewhat reduce the skin effects while maintaining an effective dose at the desired points within the body.

The precise calculation of these points needs to include the number, size and position of the radiation fields, and the use of any wedges and compensators to produce the right shapes to each of these fields. The therapy **plan** thus produced will be substantially different for each patient, and before the advent of computer-based simulators the plan took many hours of painstaking work. An example of a treatment simulation is shown in Figure 10.7.

The simulations are now produced in conjunction with cross-sectional images from X-ray computed tomography scanners (Chapter 11), which allow faster and more accurate calculation of the individual patient's treatment plan.

Brachytherapy

Some types of cancer are not readily accessible to treatment using external beams as they would involve the irradiation of too much healthy tissue. Examples include structures near the body surface

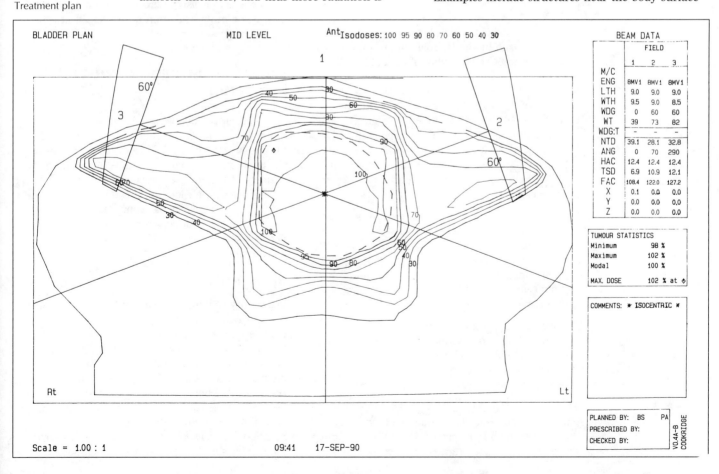

such as the eye or mouth, or near body cavities such as the cervix. In such cases the technique known as brachytherapy has proved of benefit.

This technique uses small-volume sealed sources of radioactive material positioned or implanted near the tumour to be irradiated. Radionuclides chosen for this application usually emit beta particles, and lower-energy gamma rays in the range 0.1–1 MeV. This is done to ensure that a large amount of radiation is delivered to a small volume surrounding the source, whilst causing minimal damage to more distant tissues. The most commonly used radionuclides are shown in Table 10.2.

Table 10.2

Radionuclide	Half-life	Emissions
^{192}iridium	74.4 days	beta ; gamma (0.3–0.6 MeV)
^{182}tantalum	115 days	beta ; gamma (0.07–1.2 MeV)
^{137}caesium	30 years	beta ; gamma (0.6 MeV)

Radionuclide therapy

Some radiotherapy applications use radioactive materials not in sealed sources at fixed positions, but as unsealed radionuclides. This technique relies on a radionuclide, often in a chemical compound, being taken up selectively by the part of the body which needs to be irradiated. This technique is used effectively in certain clinical situations, as outlined below.

Iodine is an element which is taken up and chemically fixed by the thyroid gland. If the thyroid becomes overactive a number of metabolic processes are affected and the condition must be treated. In this overactive state the thyroid gland takes up more iodine than normal. Relatively small doses (150–400 MBq) of ^{131}iodine are given orally, and when taken up by the thyroid will kill a proportion of the cells in the gland. This reduces the function of the gland, hopefully back to normal levels. ^{131}Iodine emits both beta particles and gamma rays, and has a half-life of 8 days.

The same technique can be used in thyroid cancer, although in this case much higher doses of ^{131}iodine are used (300–8000 MBq), often after the thyroid has been surgically removed. The high dose of the radionuclide will then kill any remaining thyroid cells in the body and try to ensure no future recurrence of the disease.

Similar techniques are sometimes used in other types of cancer. One example uses the bone-seeking properties of the radionuclide ^{89}strontium to reduce the effects of bone cancer, as it is preferentially taken up at tumour sites where it will irradiate them, killing some of the cells.

Another recent and exciting development uses antibodies which have been raised to a specific type of cancer cell. These are then labelled with a radionuclide such as ^{131}iodine. When injected into the patient, the antibody 'targets' those cancer cell types wherever they may be in the body, and attaches itself to them. The radionuclide stuck to the antibody irradiates the cells and hopefully kills them. This technique is in its infancy, but holds promise for the future.

The other major use of radionuclide therapy is in the treatment of a blood condition known as polycythaemia rubra vera. An overactive bone marrow causes an increased number of red blood cells and an increase in blood viscosity, which can put a strain on the heart and blood vessels. When ^{32}phosphorus, in doses of 100–200 MBq, is injected intravenously as sodium phosphate, it travels to the bone marrow and kills some of the cells, again reducing its activity.

Like most radionuclides used in radiotherapy, ^{32}phosphorus is a beta emitter. This means that a relatively high radiation dose per administered MBq of activity is given to the target tissues. As the beta particles only travel a short distance in tissue, the use of such radionuclides also ensures that a relatively low radiation dose is given to the surrounding tissues.

In this, as in all types of radiotherapy, the calculation and administration of the correct dose is all-important. Too little radiation will still damage healthy tissue but will not be enough to kill the cancer or other disease process, and it may well recur. Too much radiation may over-affect other normal tissues, with possibly fatal consequences.

Radiation measurement and protection

The preceding sections of this chapter give an indication of the wide range of uses of either internally administered doses of radionuclides or the application of external beams of radiation to patients. All these uses presuppose a detailed knowledge of the radiation doses the patients will receive, and the effects that may be expected as a result. The very different applications themselves demand very different types of radiation measurement.

Radionuclides

Before any radionuclide can be administered safely to a patient, we must have estimated with some confidence the radiation dose that the patient will receive as a result of the administration. The calculation of this dose involves a number of complex steps, each including assumptions regarding the behaviour of the radionuclide once injected. These steps are outlined in Figure 10.8 for one clinically useful radionuclide – ^{59}iron – mentioned earlier for its use in the study of iron kinetics. It should be noted that this type of

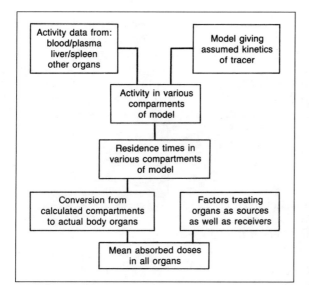

Figure 10.8
Calculation of dose to
patient for ^{59}iron study

calculation must have been performed for all
clinically used radionuclides, in whatever chemical
form they are to be administered!

The basic data for ^{59}iron are given below, together
with the dosimetric data calculated using this
model in the 'normal' case and in two types of
blood disorder:

Radionuclide:	^{59}Fe
Physical half-life:	44.5 days
Principal gamma rays:	$\begin{cases} 1.099 \text{ MeV} \\ 1.292 \text{ MeV} \end{cases}$
Beta particles:	$\begin{cases} 0.27 \text{ MeV} \\ 0.47 \text{ MeV} \end{cases}$

The absorbed dose per unit administered activity
(mGy MBq^{-1}) is given in Table 10.3.

Table 10.3

	Normal	Primary haemochromatosis*	Relapsing pernicious anaemia**
liver	12	23	16
spleen	55	82	61
red marrow	12	17	9.6
ovaries	6.4	6.3	6.3
testes	5.3	4.4	5.5
kidneys	8.6	9.6	8.4
heart wall	24	19	19

* destruction of the red cells by the liver and spleen,
** severe shortage of red cells

The figures in the table show the absorbed doses to
various organs in the body for a 'normal' patient
and patients with two notable blood disorders. It
can be seen that the radiation dose the patient
receives is subject to considerable variation,
depending on the patient's metabolism. While good
estimates of the dose received by a patient whose
body is functioning 'normally' can be made, some
disease states may produce markedly different dose
distributions. Allowance must be made for this

variation before the radionuclide may be
administered safely.

External beams

As we have seen, external beams of radiation are
used in both therapy and imaging techniques. In
all these applications two pieces of information are
crucial – the strength of the beam and its likely
dose to the patient (and hence its effect).

The measurement of exposure is clearly of great
significance as the first step towards the calculation
of the dose to the patient. However, the problems
presented in this measurement should not be
underestimated. As we have seen, a wide range of
radiation types and energies are employed.
Estimating the exposures from these different
radiations and how they impart energy to the body
tissues is a complex and ongoing task.

The size of the radiation field used and the part of
the body irradiated also greatly influence the dose
received, due to the scattering of the radiation by
the body tissues and their varying radiosensitivities.
Some of this variation can be demonstrated using
data which shows the percentage dose at different
depths of a uniform tissue-equivalent material for
three energies of diagnostic X-rays, using a source
of area 20 cm × 20 cm, as given in Table 10.4.

Table 10.4

Depth cm^{-1}	60 kV	75 kV	90 kV	100 kV
0	100	100	100	100
2	45.0	59.9	67.1	83.6
4	23.0	36.0	43.2	60.5
8	7.4	14.4	19.2	30.5
12	2.6	6.1	8.8	15.2
16	1.0	2.6	4.1	7.2

This type of data is used in the calculation of the
isodose curves for radiotherapy treatment planning.

The data presented in Table 10.4 is in fact taken
from assessments of the radiation doses from
diagnostic X-ray procedures.

These dose estimates are of equal importance to
those carried out in radiotherapy, as the tests are
applied to large numbers of the population.

Chapter 7 showed that the largest portion of the
annual radiation dose received by the population
from artificial sources comes from medical uses,
and from diagnostic X-ray procedures in particular.
Small 'dose savings' achieved in these procedures
amount to significant quantities when multiplied by
the number of such exposures made annually.

Calculations also play an important role in
ascertaining the amount of added protection in X-
ray rooms, such as lead barriers, etc., necessary to
protect both staff and members of the public from
unwanted exposure to radiation. This will be
explored further in the next chapter.

X-RAY IMAGING

X-rays in medicine

Since their discovery by Wilhelm Roentgen in 1895, the significance of X-rays has undergone a series of changes, from scientific wonder through side-show marvel to medical imaging speciality.

The medical applications of the X-ray were in fact realised very quickly, although early vintage X-ray sets were unshielded and poorly controlled. This exposed patients and hospital workers alike to large doses of radiation. Modern technology, as will be seen in this chapter, has resulted in a great deal of refinement to these techniques, which now produce high-quality images of great diagnostic value.

Production of X-rays

X-rays are produced when fast-moving electrons lose energy. In an X-ray tube this is achieved when electrons, produced by thermionic emission from a filament, are accelerated across a high potential difference and collide with a target.

When the electrons strike the target, two main types of interaction can occur. The first type involves electrons orbiting the atoms of the target material. The accelerated electrons can transfer some of their energy to the orbiting atomic electrons. This may cause the atomic electrons to be **excited**, moving them to outer orbits of the atom, or it may give them sufficient energy to leave the atom altogether, causing **ionisation**.

If the interaction involves the outer electrons of the target material, these electrons will soon return to their original orbits, releasing energy as heat.

If the interaction involves the target material's inner electrons, other electrons from outer shells of the the atom will move inwards to take their place. Figure 11.1 shows interactions of this type.

These changes in energy level result in the emission of electromagnetic radiation known as **characteristic X-radiation**. This radiation is so called because the energies of the radiation produced are characteristic of the material from which they originate.

The second type of interaction may occur when the fast-moving electrons interact not with the orbiting electrons of the target material, but with their nuclei, as Figure 11.2 shows.

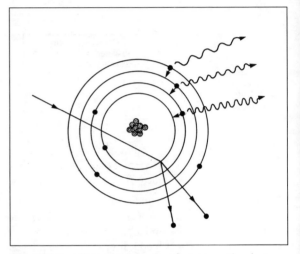

Figure 11.1   Effects of fast-moving electrons on the electrons of the target atom

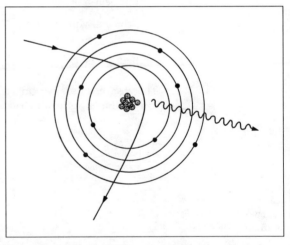

Figure 11.2   Effects of fast-moving electrons on the nucleus of the target atom, producing bremsstrahlung

If they pass close to the nucleus the attractive electrostatic force exerted by the nucleus will deflect and, most importantly, decelerate the electrons. This deceleration process results in the lost kinetic energy of the electrons being converted into electromagnetic radiation. It is known by the German name **bremsstrahlung**, meaning 'braking radiation'.

The energy of this radiation will depend on the degree of deceleration experienced by the electron, and for a number of electrons undergoing different degrees of deceleration, the radiation usually results in a continuous spectrum of X-ray energies.

The upper boundary of this spectrum depends on the magnitude of the high voltage accelerating the electrons. This is because the maximum energy of an X-ray photon would follow the loss of the total kinetic energy of the electron in one bremsstrahlung interaction. This **peak kilovoltage**, or **kVp**, although not a recognised unit, is often used as one way of describing the X-ray beam. The bremsstrahlung in fact forms the major part of the X-ray output of the tube.

It should be noted that in fact a single electron accelerated by the potential difference across the tube will undergo many of these types of interaction before losing its acquired kinetic energy.

Typically only 1% of the energy in a diagnostic X-ray tube will be converted into X-rays. The remainder appears as heat and light, since the target gets so hot that it glows.

The X-ray tube and housing

The X-ray tube

The X-ray tube basically consists of an evacuated glass envelope within which is a tungsten filament and a target, usually also made of tungsten. The target is embedded in a block of either molybdenum or copper to absorb the large quantities of heat produced. A high voltage is then applied between the filament and the target to accelerate the electrons produced by the filament. In the simplest of X-ray tubes, as used in dental X-ray sets, this would almost be the end of the story.

However, for use in other diagnostic applications, the X-ray output of such a tube is not sufficient. To achieve greater outputs a different design of tube is required, using a **rotating anode**, Figure 11.3.

The rotating anode consists of a disc of molybdenum, approximately 100 mm in diameter,

bevelled around the edge to an angle of 16–17°. On this bevelled edge is a circular ring some 6 mm wide, containing the tungsten–rhenium alloy target material. The whole anode assembly is rotated using an induction motor at typically 9000 revolutions per minute.

The advantage of this type of design over the stationary anode is that because of the rotation, the heat loading at any point on the target is reduced. It is therefore possible to use higher potential differences across the tube and higher tube currents without the danger of melting the target, adding to the versatility of the X-ray tube.

The bevelled angle of the anode and target means that the majority of the X-rays are emitted downwards and out of the tube and its housing. Nevertheless, much of the housing is lead lined to absorb any stray radiation produced in other directions.

The tube housing

The housing is designed to allow the tube to be supported and to provide suitable points for the high and low voltage connections. The housing is usually oil filled to aid heat removal from the tube assembly, and to provide a very effective electrical insulation medium. It incorporates a thermal cut-out switch so that if the tube (and hence the oil) gets too hot, the oil expands and cuts the power to the tube. This also prevents damage to the target due to overheating.

Immediately below the main housing is placed an aluminium filter, approximately 2.5 mm thick. This is designed to absorb any low-energy X-radiation being emitted by the tube. The low-energy radiation is not energetic enough to be transmitted through the patient and reach the film. If it were not absorbed by the aluminium it would therefore add to the patient's radiation dose without contributing to the image quality.

Below this is usually positioned a device known as a **light–beam diaphragm**, or **LBD**. The LBD consists of two pairs of moveable shutters, usually known as **leaves**, at right angles to each other. The leaves are made of lead and are used to adjust the size of the X-ray beam by absorbing any radiation that does not pass through the rectangular opening in their centre. Within the LBD housing is a lamp and a half-silvered mirror transluscent to X-radiation. Light from the lamp is reflected down through the opening between the leaves, and allows the radiographer to optically position the area that will be exposed to the X-rays.

The X-ray spectrum

The usual potential differences used in the production of diagnostic X-rays are in the range 20–120 kV. However, because of the bremsstrahlung process, most of the X-radiation

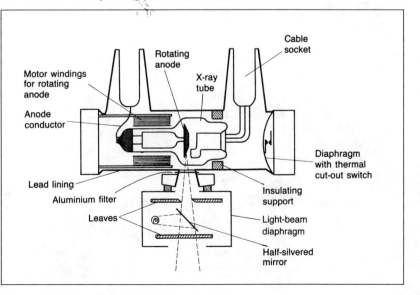

Figure 11.3   X-ray tube with rotating anode

emitted will be at a considerably lower energy, the peak usually occurring between a third and a half of the maximum energy. Increasing the high voltage across the tube increases both the number of X-rays and their maximum energy, as Figure 11.4(a) shows.

The effect of the aluminium filter on the X-ray spectrum is dramatic, as seen in Figure 11.4(b). The removal of the low-energy X-radiation greatly reduces the overall intensity of the beam, particularly as the lower energies are the most abundant. The other major effect of filtering out the low-energy radiation is to increase the average energy of the X-rays for any given peak energy value.

The high-voltage generator

The simplest type of circuit used for providing the high-voltage supply is shown in Figure 11.5.

One important component in the circuit is a step-up transformer for the production of the high voltage itself. However, a single transformer would not easily be capable of providing a number of different high voltages. For this reason an autotransformer is used to make adjustments to the size of the mains voltage prior to its multiplication in the step-up transformer. A small filament transformer supplies the necessary current for the cathode. The principal way of controlling the intensity of the X-ray beam is achieved by varying the number of electrons accelerated across the X-ray tube. In theory, this would simply be accomplished by increasing the tube current (usually measured in milliamperes, mA). In practice, however, increasing the tube current in this way would run the great risk of overheating the anode and causing severe damage. To prevent this from happening, the current is usually varied between a number of fixed values using a multi-position switch incorporating a set of different resistances.

It should be noted that the supply to the X-ray tube is an alternating voltage. Therefore, when using the simple circuit of Figure 11.5, only when the anode is positive with respect to the cathode will X-rays be produced. During the other half of the cycle the tube will be largely inactive, unless the target is hot enough to produce its own thermionic emissions (which might damage the filament). In addition, the exact value of the high voltage will be varying greatly over the useful half-cycle, as Figure 11.6 demonstrates.

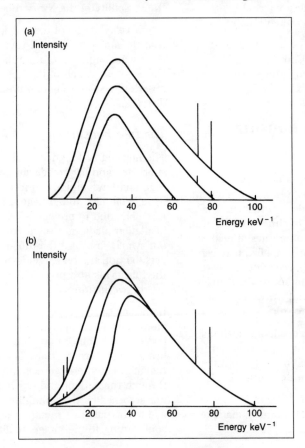

Figure 11.4
(a) Increasing the tube voltage (b) Increasing the beam filtration

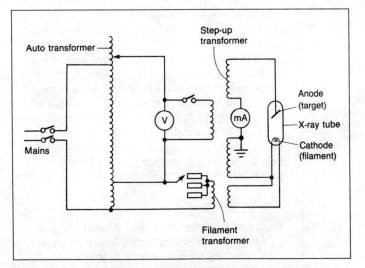

Figure 11.5   Circuit for producing high-voltage supply

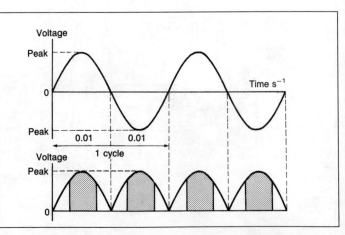

Figure 11.6   Periods (shaded) when the circuit of Figure 11.5 produces X-rays

This situation can be greatly improved with the use of a four-diode 'bridge' circuit. This provides rectification of the alternating voltage over the full cycle, and this **full-wave rectification** allows a much more unidirectional potential to reach the X-ray tube. The additional use of capacitors provides further 'smoothing' of the high voltage, keeping it as constant as possible during the exposure.

Large modern X-ray systems provide extra smoothness in the high voltage by using a **three-phase supply**. This effectively triples the frequency of the mains supply, and following suitable rectification and smoothing provides a virtually constant potential high-voltage supply.

Attenuation

When a beam of X- (or gamma) rays passes through matter, its energy will be gradually deposited in the material, and hence the intensity of the beam will be diminished. For a monoenergetic beam this **attenuation** means that equal thicknesses of an homogeneous absorber remove equal percentages of the beam's energy. Mathematically this can be written:

$$I_x = I_0 \, e^{-\mu x}$$

Where: I_0 is the initial intensity of the beam,

I_x is the intensity at a thickness x in the material, and

μ is the linear attenuation coefficient

This equation is of the same form as the exponential decay process for radioactivity (Chapter 7). In this equation μ, the linear attenuation coefficient, is the fraction of X-rays removed from the beam per unit thickness of the medium through which it is passing. The actual value of μ depends on both the energy of the radiation and the material itself.

In a way also analogous to radioactive decay, where we talk of the 'half-life', we can derive the '**half-value thickness**' – the thickness of a material that will diminish the intensity of the X-ray beam of a specified energy to one-half its original level.

However, the physical state of the material – whether it is a solid, liquid or gas – will also have an effect on the attenuating power of the material, as in the solid form there are more atoms per unit volume of the material for the photons to interact with. For this reason a quantity known as the **total mass attenuation coefficient** is sometimes used. This is defined as the fraction of X-rays removed from a beam of unit cross-sectional area in a medium of unit mass, and is μ/d, where d is the density of the material. The advantage of using the total mass attenuation coefficient as opposed to

the linear attenuation coefficient is that the former is by definition independent of the density of the material in question.

It should be noted that the above equations and descriptions deal with essentially *monochromatic* radiation – that is, radiation of a single energy/wavelength. As we have seen, in the real-life situation of X-ray production the beam is in fact *heterogeneous* – it is composed of a large range of energies/wavelengths.

Interaction of X-rays with matter

This section will deal with how energy is lost from the X-ray beam. Two main processes are involved in this attenuation – **photoelectric absorption** and **scattering**.

Photoelectric absorption

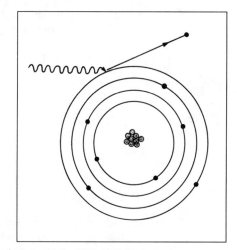

Figure 11.7   Photoelectric absorption

In this process, an X-ray photon interacts with an orbiting electron of an atom of the material through which it is passing. In the interaction all the energy of the photon is transferred to the electron, which is then ejected from the atom, Figure 11.7. The resulting ionised atom will regain the steady state as the other orbiting electrons rearrange themselves to fill any gaps, with the emission of lower-energy radiation characteristic of the jumps in energy level that the electrons make.

The degree of photoelectric absorption taking place within a material through which an X-ray beam passes depends on the energy of the beam and the material itself. The probability of photoelectric absorption increases with the proton number of the absorber material (in fact varying as Z^3). However, as the energy of the beam increases, photoelectric absorption becomes less likely (varying as $1/E^3$). For X-ray beams of energies commonly used for diagnostic purposes, photoelectric absorption is the major attenuating process.

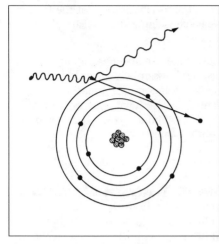

Figure 11.8   Compton scattering

Scattering

Scattering processes come in two basic types. The first of these is known by a variety of names: 'elastic', 'classical', 'coherent' or 'Rayleigh'. In this process the X-ray photon is deflected from its path by interacting with an electron orbiting an atom of the absorber material, but without losing any of its energy. Elastic scattering occurs only at low photon energies, and plays little role in the attenuation of a diagnostic X-ray beam.

The other process, shown in Figure 11.8, is known as Compton scattering. Here the photon interacts with an outer orbiting electron of the absorber's atom. The photon is again deflected by the electron, but in Compton scattering some of the photon's energy is transferred to the electron, ejecting it from the atom. The greater the angle through which the photon is scattered, the greater the loss of its energy.

The probability of Compton scattering occurring gradually decreases as the energy of the photons increase (varying as $1/E$). It is also dependent on the density of electrons in the absorb-ing material, but not on the proton number, Z.

Interaction of X-rays with tissue

A beam of X-rays of diagnostic energy interacts with living tissue principally by the processes of photoelectric absorption and Compton scattering described above. However, different types of tissue have markedly different compositions, and this will be reflected in the way they attenuate the X-ray beam.

If we compare soft tissues such as muscle and fat with bone, for example, two significant differences emerge in the way they attenuate X-rays. The average proton number for soft tissue is approximately 7, whereas the value for bone is nearer 14. This is because soft tissue is mainly composed of lighter elements such as carbon, hydrogen and oxygen, whereas bone has significant quantities of both calcium ($Z = 20$) and phosphorus ($Z = 15$) in addition to the lighter elements.

The second factor is density. The density of soft tissues is very nearly 1.0, whereas the average density of bone is approximately 1.8.

The strong dependence of photoelectric absorption on Z (Z^3) means that this type of interaction is far more likely to occur in bone than in soft tissue. The greater density of bone will compound this difference, and means that a given thickness of

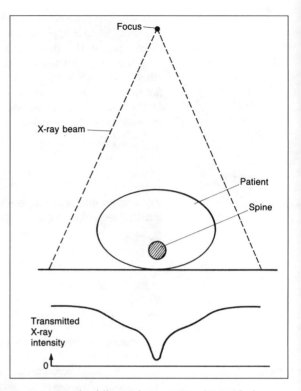

Figure 11.9   The differential attenuation of X-rays by bone and soft tissues

bone will attenuate the X-ray beam far more than the same thickness of soft tissue, Figure 11.9.

It is this difference in transmitted intensity of the X-ray beam which forms the basis of its use in medical imaging.

X-ray imaging

Film and the intensifying screen

In Chapter 9 the use of film as a detector of ionising radiation was described. This use was based on the fact that the degree of blackening at a point on a piece of developed film was directly related to the radiation exposure the film received prior to development.

Therefore, if a sheet of film is placed under a patient, and the patient (and film) then exposed to a beam of X-rays, the variations in transmitted intensity produced by the patient will be reproduced on the film. The difficulty with this simple idea is the relative insensitivity of film to X-rays. To produce a satisfactory image on the film would require quite a large exposure to the X-rays.

The modern imaging department circumvents this particular problem by the use of the so-called **intensifying cassette**, Figure 11.10.

The cassette sandwiches a sheet of film between two flat fluorescent screens. The screens are made of white plastic onto which are glued thin layers of fluorescent crystals covered with a scratch-proof

Figure 11.10   X-ray film cassette with intensifying screen

lacquer to prevent damage. The screens are kept in close contact with the film when the cassette is shut. The back of the cassette includes a metal plate to absorb any radiation passing through the film and screens. This prevents any radiation being scattered back from the couch (between the patient and film) or beyond onto the film and thus degrading the image.

When the cassette is exposed to X-rays, the fluorescent crystals absorb the X-radiation and re-emit larger numbers of light photons. As the film is more sensitive to light than to X-rays, a significant gain in film blackening is therefore achieved for the same X-ray exposure. This gain, known as the **intensification factor**, can easily exceed 100.

Two different types of intensifying screen are in common usage. The older type uses calcium tungstate ($CaWO_4$) as the phosphor. This has relatively good X-ray absorption due to its high average proton number, and a good output of blue light. These factors produce an intensification factor of 30–90 depending on factors such as the X-ray energy used.

The second and more recent type of intensifying screen uses rare-earth elements. One typical example is gadolinium oxysulphide with a terbium impurity ($Gd_2O_2S{:}Tb$). The higher proton numbers of gadolinium ($Z = 64$) and terbium ($Z = 65$) give this type of screen a higher absorption of X-rays, and in addition this phosphor has a high efficiency of production of green light. This combination produces intensification factors for the screen of up to 250, and this improved performance makes the rare-earth screen the system of choice.

The great advantage of the intensifying screen is that the increased light intensity enables high-quality images to be obtained at a much shorter exposure (and hence lower radiation dose to the patient) than would be possible with the plain film.

Contrast enhancement

In many types of X-ray investigation there is a large degree of contrast between the part of the body being investigated and its surrounding tissue. Striking examples of this occur when looking for fractures in a limb, or in chest radiography where the air in the lungs is much less attenuating than the surrounding ribs and vertebrae.

However, many of the different types of body tissue such as blood, muscle, kidneys and the gastrointestinal tract have very similar densities and elemental compositions. As such there is very little radiographic contrast between these tissues, and their investigation using simple differences in X-ray transmission would therefore present a number of problems. The solution to many of these difficulties is accomplished by administering an artificial **contrast medium** to the patient.

The most frequently used contrast media use solutions containing high proton-number elements such as barium or iodine. Examples of these compounds are barium sulphate or organic iodine compounds such as sodium iothalamate or sodium diatrizoate.

The contrast medium may be administered to the patient in a number of ways. In the well-known (or infamous!) 'barium meal' the patient swallows a thick suspension containing barium sulphate. As this passes through various sections of the gastro-intestinal tract, a series of images can be taken. The contrast medium absorbs more of the X-ray beam than the surrounding tissue and thus delineates the gastrointestinal tract.

In another example contrast media using organic iodine compounds can be used to visualise the arterial or venous blood supply to a particular organ by injecting the medium directly into the blood vessel concerned. The structure and effective flow diameter of the vessels can then be seen following a series of rapidly taken films.

In this and in all such uses of contrast media a number of criteria have to be satisfied before the material can be used:

(a) The medium must be non-toxic and safe.
(b) It must produce sufficient contrast to accurately outline the organ or vessels of interest.
(c) It should have the correct viscosity, miscibility and excretion rate. These properties may vary enormously depending on the site in which the medium is to be used.

External factors affecting imaging

Intensity and tube current

In general terms, the diagnostic quality of a radiographic image will be directly related to the numbers of X-ray photons (i.e. beam intensity) reaching the film. Radiation dose considerations will necessarily limit this exposure (see below), but within these limits different examinations and different patients will require different exposures and thus beam intensities.

As we saw earlier, in modern X-ray systems the tube current is restricted to a small number of fixed settings. The amount of X-ray exposure received by the patient is therefore usually varied by increasing or decreasing the time for which the electrons are produced by the filament.

The X-ray exposure is thus measured by the product of tube current and exposure time, and this usually has the units of milliampere-second, or mA s.

Beam 'quality'

The 'quality ' of an X-ray beam is a term used to describe the beam's penetrating power. Increasing the peak voltage across the X-ray tube (kVp) increases the maximum energy of the X-rays in the beam. Both photoelectric absorption and Compton scattering processes decrease in probability with increasing X-ray energy. Therefore, providing the filtration does not change, increasing the kVp will increase the beam's penetrating power or 'quality'.

It should be noted that increasing the kVp gives a fixed number of electrons more energy. This in turn means that a greater number of X-rays will be produced at the target, and thus the intensity of the beam will also be increased. The intensity of the beam is in fact proportional to the square of the peak kilovoltage.

The quality of the X-ray beam dramatically changes the type of image produced. As the kVp is increased, the proportion of the beam attenuated by photoelectric absorption becomes less. This leads to a decrease in the difference in transmitted intensity between bone and soft tissue, and thus a decrease in image contrast. When taking a radiograph, care must therefore be exercised to use a sufficiently high kVp to penetrate the structures to be investigated (particularly in larger patients), but not too high to decrease the resolution of fine structures within the patient.

On the other hand, when studying organs such as the female breast (known as mammography), where small differences in attenuation can be crucial, image contrast is maximised by using very low kVps.

Focal spot size

The ability of an X-ray imaging system to record fine structures in the patient will depend on the degree of geometrical unsharpness present. One of the main causes of this unsharpness is the apparent size of the source of X-rays at the target.

The focal spot can be made smaller in one of two ways. The first of these is to use a smaller, more focused beam of electrons, Figure 11.11.

The second method uses a change in the angle of the anode relative to the direction of the electron beam. Increasing this angle decreases the size of the focal spot.

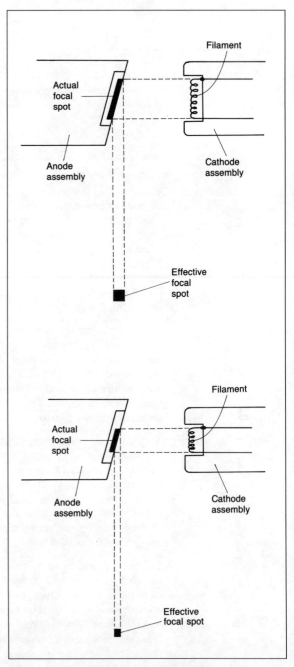

Figure 11.11   Varying the focal spot size by focusing the beam of electrons

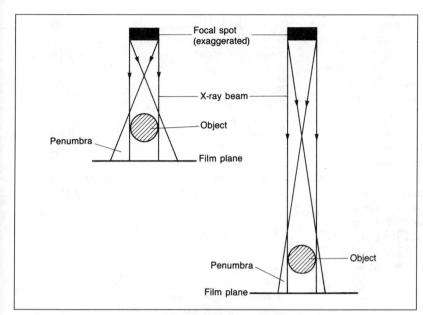

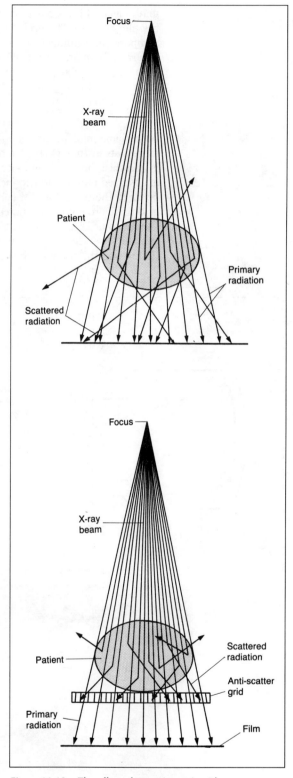

Figure 11.12
The effect of FFD on
sharpness of image

Both methods are effective, but the same number of electrons hitting a smaller target area leads to a greater heat density in the target when compared with a larger focal spot. The only way of avoiding this problem is to reduce the number of electrons hitting the target by reducing the tube current. This results in longer exposure times to recover the loss of beam intensity, and causes increased tube wear.

Distance

Another cause of geometrical unsharpness is the distance between the focal spot and the patient and film. This distance is often known by the terms **focus-to-skin distance (FSD)** and **focus-to-film distance (FFD)**.

This type of unsharpness can be minimised by increasing the FFD, Figure 11.2, although it should be realised that an X-ray beam, like any other point source of electromagnetic radiation, is subject to the inverse square law. Thus the intensity of the beam is reduced in proportion to the square of the distance from the source. Increasing the FFD therefore reduces the beam intensity and requires the use of more penetrating radiation and/or a longer exposure time to achieve the same film blackening. In practice the FFD is usually of the order of 1 metre.

It should be noted that the object-to-film distance must remain the same while increasing the FFD for there to be any benefit in image quality.

Scattered radiation

Scattered radiation increases the radiation dose to both patients and staff who are present, and also degrades the quality of the radiograph. It does this by causing a general loss of contrast in the film, since the scatter tends to move in non-specific directions.

Figure 11.13   The effect of an anti-scatter grid

Unless preventative measures were taken, this image degradation would be likely to limit the usefulness of the X-ray techniques and their diagnostic accuracy since small, poorly defined structures might be lost in the general 'fogging'.

In practice this scattered radiation is almost totally (80–90%) removed using a device known as a

grid, Figure 11.13, placed between the patient and the film cassette. The grid is basically a thin sheet composed of a number of slats of lead foil, separated by material translucent to X-rays. The slats stand on edge pointing towards the X-ray source and absorb almost all X-radiation deflected from its original path.

The exact number of slats varies between 3 and 10 per millimetre, depending on the grid design. The more slats in the grid the more scattered radiation is absorbed, but also the more unscattered radiation is absorbed too, due to the increased area of lead between the patient and the film. The use of the grid therefore entails an increase in the exposure needed to produce sufficient film blackening, and thus an increase in the patient's radiation dose. For this reason the use and choice of grid must be made with caution.

Each of the lead slats must be as thin as possible to avoid casting a shadow on the film, but there is a minimum thickness below which the effectiveness of the grid is significantly reduced.

To avoid the problem of the grid itself causing difficulties in interpretation of the image, in many cases the grid is made to move during the exposure. The mechanism, known as a 'Bucky' after one of its originators, usually makes the grid move in an oscillatory fashion. The movement allows the grid to absorb the scattered radiation but blurs the shadows that would be cast by the slats.

Fluoroscopy

We have so far considered only those applications where images have been taken of static structures, such as the skull, chest or a fractured limb. In many cases, however, we would like to investigate dynamic processes. This is particularly true for studies involving the use of contrast media, such as blood flow studies or the use of the barium meal for gastrointestinal function.

This can be, and indeed is, sometimes done by taking a series of 'snapshots' using fast film-changing devices and standard radiographic apparatus. Another approach, known as **fluoroscopy**, uses the concept of a continuous beam of X-rays, made visible using a fluorescent screen.

In its early days this was exactly how the technique was used. However, the relative inefficiency of the screen meant that a very dark room and a high X-ray intensity was needed to ensure good anatomical visibility, giving the patient a large radiation dose.

The use of a device known as an **image intensifier**, Figure 11.14, can produce images over a thousand times brighter than the original screen. This allows radiation doses to be cut by up to 90% of the unintensified value.

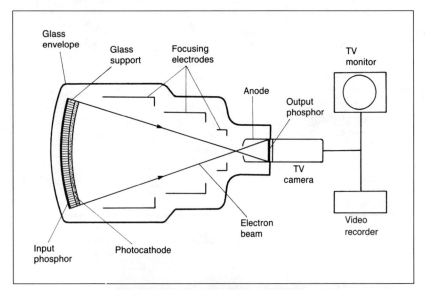

The image intensifier uses an evacuated glass tube up to 30 cm in diameter. A fluorescent screen is placed at one end in direct contact with a photocathode. This combination converts the X-rays first to visible photons and then to electrons. The number of electrons at any point on the photocathode is directly proportional to the X-ray intensity at that point on the phosphor, and hence to the transmitted intensity through the patient.

The electrons produced by the photocathode are then accelerated through a potential difference of approximately 20 kV, using a series of focusing anodes. This acceleration and concentration of the electrons results in a relatively large number arriving at another fluorescent screen at the far end, producing a much brighter image. This image is usually picked up by a television camera which

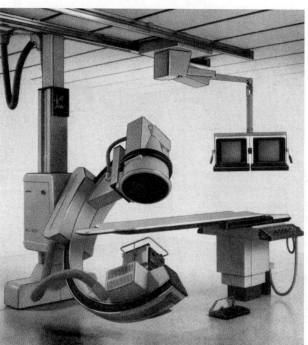

Figure 11.14
An image
intensifier

can then relay the signal to a monitor screen or video recording device.

The use of such electron and photon optics in the image intensifier means that care must be taken in its design to minimise distortion and maximise the resolution of fine detail.

Fluoroscopy is a technique which is used sparingly, as even using good image intensification the radiation dose to the patient is significantly higher than from a standard radiographic examination, due to the greater overall exposure time. Dose 'savings' can be made by using short bursts of X-rays rather than a truly continuous exposure, but even so the examinations remain relatively dose-intensive.

Computed tomography

The human body is not arranged conveniently for examinations using either radiographic or fluoroscopic techniques. The different body structures overlap in a complex three-dimensional volume. As such an X-ray beam can be subject to transmission through many of these structures, each with their own degree of attenuation. In addition, some scattered radiation will get to the image, causing further degradation.

One way to reduce some of these problems is to only transmit the X-ray beam through one thin 'slice' at a time. This is done in the technique known as **computerised axial tomography**, now shortened to **computerised tomography** or **CT**.

The technique was invented in the early 1970s, and with the growth of computer technology has subsequently undergone much development. Different CT scanning machines have been produced, using slightly varied approaches.

Perhaps the most common design is illustrated in Figure 11.15.

In this design a well collimated fan-shaped beam of X-rays, typically 2–10 mm thick, is transmitted through the patient. The X-rays are detected by an array of small detectors arranged in a circular arc. The detectors are usually scintillation crystals such as sodium iodide (thallium) or a semiconductor such as bismuth germanate.

The whole source/detector assembly is rotated around a central circular hole containing the patient over a period of approximately 1–15 seconds. As the assembly rotates, the X-ray tube produces a series of short pulses of radiation. The detectors pick up the transmitted intensities at each point, storing them in a computer memory. Following the 'scan', as it is called, the computer then reconstructs an image from the 200 000– 500 000 or more individual readings of transmitted intensity. For this to be done within a matter of seconds requires a high-speed minicomputer.

The technique is based on the fact that each intensity reading is composed of the sum of the linear attenuation coefficients of the materials through which the X-ray beam has passed en route to the detector. The reconstruction process is known as 'back projection', as the computer effectively projects each of the transmitted intensities back into an 'image space', building up a picture of the structures that have been scanned.

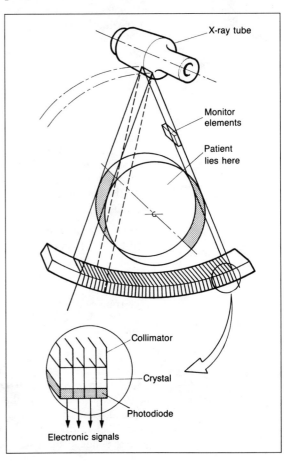

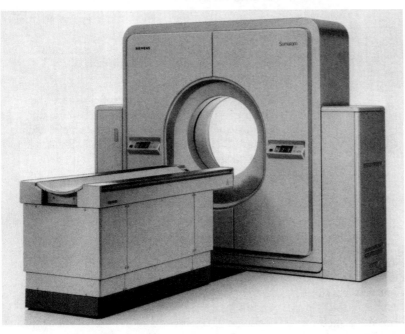

Figure 11.15   CT scanning machine

Taking a series of axial (perpendicular to the long axis of the patient) 'slices' in this way, detailed information can be built up of the patient's internal anatomy in three dimensions. Details of the order of 1–2 mm can be resolved, and differences of just 1% in the attenuation coefficient are identifiable.

Radiation doses from such investigations are significantly higher than in standard radiography, but this is compensated somewhat by the detailed diagnostic information obtainable from the images.

Radiation dose to patients and staff

Patients

As we saw in Chapter 8, it is currently assumed that all doses of radiation are capable of producing harm in the person being exposed. For this reason, if we deliberately expose someone to radiation, as in an X-ray examination, we must be assured that the likely benefit arising from the exposure outweighs the risk of that exposure. We must also do everything possible to reduce that risk to as low a level as possible, by using the minimum amount of radiation consistent with getting the information required to make an accurate diagnosis of the patient's condition.

As for all radiation usage, we must use the principles of justification and optimisation. Justification means asking the right questions, such as: 'Is the test necessary?', 'What information will we obtain?', 'Will it usefully affect the treatment of the patient?', 'Can we obtain equally useful information without exposing the patient to radiation?'.

Optimisation means using the minimum radiation possible to obtain good quality images. It also requires good technique from the person taking the X-ray images to cut down on the numbers of repeat exposures and to collimate the beam so that only the part of the body that needs to be exposed is exposed.

Additional quality checks are achieved by ensuring that the exposures made in one hospital are consistent with those made in another, by assessing the factors that go into the different types of investigation, and by continuous checks on the performance of the imaging equipment.

Staff

As well as limiting the radiation dose received by the patient undergoing the investigation, it is important to minimise the dose received by the staff performing them. While the patient may only be exposed a few times during the course of the investigation, the staff will perform many such examinations every day.

This limitation is mainly achieved by distance and shielding. X-ray rooms are designed such that the walls are sufficiently attenuating that no significant exposure can take place to anyone standing behind them. Within the room, the operator usually stands behind a screen made from a laminate of wood and lead sheets. Glass in the screen has added lead to provide high attenuation of the X-ray beam.

The operator sometimes has to stand outside the protected area during an exposure, such as in a fluoroscopic examination, when the patient may be moved under the beam to watch the passage of the contrast medium. In these circumstances the staff must wear a lead 'apron', reducing the radiation dose to the torso and gonads.

The exact amount of added protection necessary must be determined by measuring or estimating the X-ray exposure at the particular places involved. As this can be difficult to achieve with the necessary accuracy, the usual procedure is to measure the exposure close to the source of the X-rays, and apply the inverse square law to calculate the exposure at the given distance.

Knowing that exposure level and the half-value thickness of lead for the energy of the X-rays used, it is possible to calculate the necessary thickness of lead (or lead equivalent material) to be added which will reduce the exposure to an acceptable level.

Thus, an X-ray source may have an exposure rate of 500 $\mu C\ kg^{-1}\ h^{-1}$ at a distance of 1 m.

Using the inverse square law, the exposure rate at a distance of x metres will be proportional to $1/x^2$.

Thus, at 2 m, the exposure rate will be proportional to $1/2^2\ (= 1/4)$ of the original exposure rate, or 125 $\mu C\ kg^{-1}\ h^{-1}$.

Doubling the distance again reduces the original exposure rate by a further factor of 4, to 31.25 $\mu C\ kg^{-1}\ h^{-1}$. It may thus be seen that distance is a useful way of reducing X-ray exposure.

To achieve the same reduction factor of 16, but staying at the original distance of 1 m, would require additional protection from some shielding material. This would amount to 4 half-value thicknesses:

$$\tfrac{1}{2} \times \tfrac{1}{2}\ (=\tfrac{1}{4}) \times \tfrac{1}{2}\ (=\tfrac{1}{8}) \times \tfrac{1}{2}\ (=\tfrac{1}{16})$$

The actual value would of course depend on the material used and the X-ray energy, as stated above.

X-ray imaging – practical cases

Figure 11.16 shows a patient being prepared for a standard X-ray investigation of the abdomen. After the patient is made comfortable and stable on the

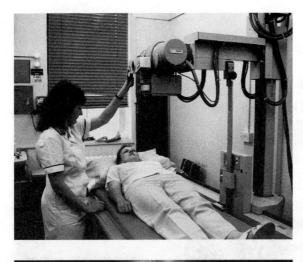

Figure 11.16
Preparing for an X-ray
examination

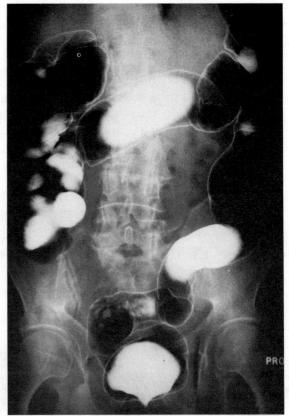

Figure 11.18   'Barium meal' image of abdomen

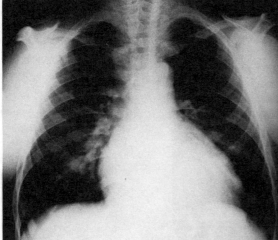

Figure 11.17
Chest X-ray

imaging table, the X-ray tube housing is positioned over the correct area to be X-rayed using the light beam diaphragm.

Figure 11.17 shows a chest X-ray image. In this study the key feature is in fact the dark area of little X-ray attenuation in the air-filled lung fields. The rib cage can be seen encircling the lungs. The large white area below and between the lungs is the heart, liver and abdomen. The original film shows a wealth of detail in the lung fields, and experienced observers routinely use such films to help diagnose conditions as varied as infection to cancer, by looking at the different patterns of X-ray attenuation.

Figure 11.18 shows a standard X-ray image of the abdomen and pelvis taken using a contrast medium (the so-called barium meal). Superimposed on the bony skeleton can be seen the large intestine. The white areas within the intestine are patches of the barium contrast agent, whereas the dark areas are packets of gas. A series of such films is usually taken during the examination to show the passage of the contrast medium, revealing any problems in transit or other abnormalities.

Figure 11.19 shows an axial computed tomographic (CT) 'slice' through the head of the

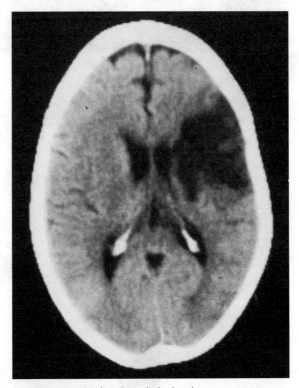

Figure 11.19   CT slice through the head

patient. The main feature of the image is a large blood clot (the dark area of lesser X-ray attenuation towards the upper right part of the image).

Figure 11.20 shows an axial computed tomographic (CT) 'slice' through the abdomen of a patient. The main feature on the left of the image shows the liver of the patient. This contains a number of dark circular areas, which represent the sites of secondary tumours which have invaded the normal liver tissue. The white areas surrounding the image are the ribs and one of the vertebrae.

Figure 11.21 shows a three-dimensional computer image of the bones in the knee. It has been reconstructed by the imaging computer from a series of axial computed tomographic (CT) 'slices'.

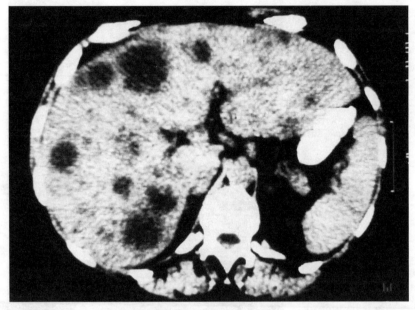

Figure 11.20   CT slice through the abdomen

Figure 11.21   Reconstructed CT image of the knee

Questions

1. a) Draw a typical spectrum of the X-radiation produced from the target of a diagnostic X-ray tube. Indicate on your diagram that part of the spectrum usually removed by filtration. Explain the reason why filters are used and suggest a suitable material for such a filter.

   b) List *three* factors which affect the quality of a radiographic image produced by X-rays. Explain how, instead of allowing the radiation to form an image directly on suitable film, it is possible to reduce the absorbed dose to the patient and still obtain a photographic image of the same density.

   (JMB – part question)

2. State, without explanation, *three* methods which are used for minimising the absorbed dose to patients during diagnostic radiography.

   Calculate the ratio of the transmitted to the incident intensities of an X-ray beam travelling through a layer of aluminium 2 mm thick, the half-value thickness being 3 mm. (JMB – part question)

3. a) In order to obtain a correctly exposed X-ray film of the chest of an average-sized patient, the tube voltage, V, is set at 65 kV and the tube current, I, at 500 mA. If the tube voltage is increased to 80 kV, how will the current have to be changed in order to keep the exposure constant, assuming the exposure time remains unchanged? (At a particular point in air the X-ray beam intensity may be assumed to vary as the product $V^2 I$.)

   b) Sketch curves to illustrate the variation of X-ray intensity with X-ray photon energy (or with X-ray wavelength) for tube voltages of 65 kV and 80 kV and point out any significant features. (The X-ray tube has a tungsten target.) How would the quality of the radiation change when the tube voltage is increased from 65 kV to 80 kV?

   c) Just after emerging from the X-ray tube itself the X-ray beam is often made to pass through a thin sheet of aluminium. For what purpose is this done?

   d) What changes would you make in order to produce a correctly exposed X-ray film for the chest of a very fat person, bearing in mind the need for adequate radiological protection for the patient? (ULSEB – part question)

12 RADIONUCLIDE IMAGING

From tracers to radionuclide imaging

In many ways, radionuclide imaging was a natural development of the radioactive tracer studies discussed in Chapter 10. Having first used these radioactive tracers in sampling and then in counting studies such as the ^{131}iodine thyroid uptake, the next logical step forward was to 'map' the numbers of counts recorded from a series of locations within the body.

The use of more finely focused collimated detectors meant that the increments of movement from count to count could be dramatically reduced. With the mechanisation of this process, and the use of more sophisticated display methods, these count maps could be turned into images of the distribution of the radionuclide.

Radionuclide imaging devices

The rectilinear scanner

The **rectilinear scanner** was the first instrument to mechanise the process of radionuclide image formation. Initial versions of the scanner consisted of a single scintillation crystal and photomultiplier tube assembly, with a multiple-hole collimator focused typically to a point 5–10 cm away from the front of the collimator, Figure 12.1(a).

As its name implies, the rectilinear scanner builds up its image by a process of scanning backwards and forwards linearly across the part of the patient to be imaged, with a small step along the patient in between each scanning pass.

As the detector moves across the patient, the count rate detected during each part of the movement is transmitted as an electronic signal to a small lamp mechanically linked to the position of the detector. The lamp then gradually exposes a sheet of film. The number of counts recorded from the patient are directly related to the brightness of the lamp, and hence the blackening of the film at the corresponding location.

The accuracy of a radionuclide image formed by this or any other imaging device is directly related to the number of counts recorded at any given image location. For the rectilinear scanner this depends on the activity of the radionuclide administered and the time spent at each location. For a whole-body image such as Figure 12.1(b), the total scanning time might amount to 45 minutes per image, with the scanner moving at

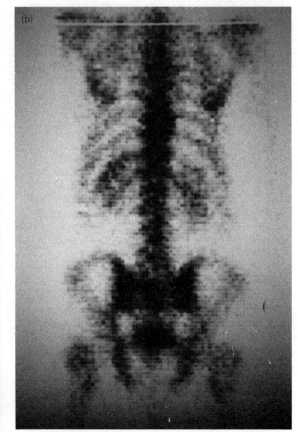

Figure 12.1
(a) Rectilinear scanner
(b) Radionuclide image of the skeleton

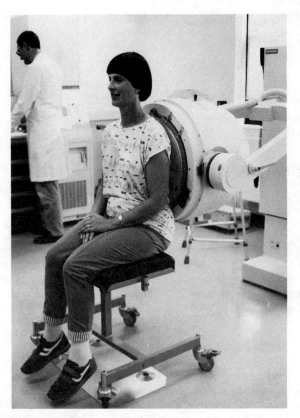

Figure 12.2
Gamma camera

more than 2 cm s^{-1}. Two 'views' – images from specific directions – would usually be done, one from the back and one from the front.

One major improvement to the design of the rectilinear scanner added a second detection system facing in the opposite direction to the first. This allows the two 'views' to be acquired simultaneously, halving the previous total scanning time.

Nevertheless, the rectilinear scanner suffers from drawbacks inherent in its design. Principal amongst these is the relatively long time it takes to build up an image of a particular area within the patient. This leads to problems in keeping ill patients sufficiently still during the course of the lengthy imaging process. Most importantly, however, it means that a **dynamic** process – imaging the movement of a tracer through a particular bodily system – cannot be observed using the rectilinear scanner unless the process is very slow moving.

The gamma camera

The **gamma camera** solves this problem of gradual area build-up by simultaneously acquiring counts over a larger field of view. First developed in 1957 in America by H.O. Anger, the key element of the gamma camera (or Anger camera as it is often known) consists of a large diameter sodium iodide crystal, now typically 400 mm in diameter and 9 mm thick. Figures 12.2 and 12.3 show the setup.

Behind the crystal, and coupled to it, are a large number of photomultiplier (PM)-tubes in a hexagonal close-packed array. The exact number of PM-tubes varies considerably between different manufacturers, but 61 or 75 tubes are typical.

When a gamma ray strikes the crystal and its energy is absorbed within it, differing amounts of the light from the resultant scintillation will reach several of the PM-tubes. The electronic signals from these PM-tubes are compared, and from this comparison an estimate of the position of the point of gamma-ray absorption is obtained.

This estimate is fed as an 'X' and 'Y' signal to the plates of an oscilloscope. A signal comprised of the total light intensity is fed simultaneously into a pulse-height analyser. If this pulse falls within an acceptable window (range of gamma-ray energies), a so-called 'Z' pulse is produced. This switches on the oscilloscope beam and allows the 'X' and 'Y' signals to produce a spot on the screen at a position corresponding to the position of the gamma ray on the crystal.

The oscilloscope flashes are usually photographed using a long exposure period sufficient to build up an image of the distribution of the radioactive material corresponding to that seen by the gamma camera.

However, in this format the gamma camera would not prove a very useful imaging instrument unless

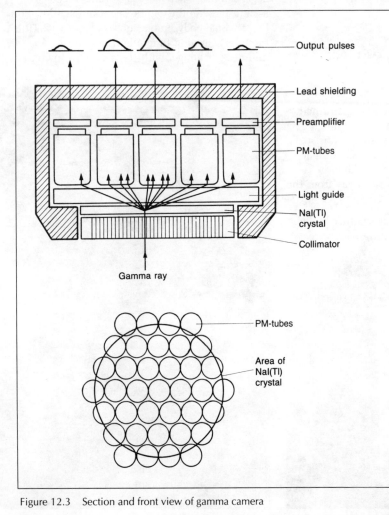

Figure 12.3   Section and front view of gamma camera

Output pulses
Lead shielding
Preamplifier
PM-tubes
Light guide
NaI(Tl) crystal
Collimator
Gamma ray
PM-tubes
Area of NaI(Tl) crystal

Figure 12.4
Collimator

the radioactive source was very close to the face of the scintillation crystal. This is because gamma rays from the source would strike almost all of the crystal with virtually equal intensity. For this reason, the front face of the crystal is usually shrouded by a removable collimator, most commonly composed of many thousands of parallel-sided holes interspersed with lead, Figure 12.4.

The collimator acts in a very similar way to the 'grid' used in X-ray imaging techniques, in that it only allows gamma rays from specific (in this case orthogonal) directions to strike the crystal. Gamma rays from all other directions are absorbed by the lead **septa** in the collimator and do not register. This achieves reasonably good spatial definition (resolution is typically 3 mm), but at the expense of a large reduction in the sensitivity of the detector to radiation.

Varying the number and size of the holes produces a range of collimators with different characteristics. A smaller number of larger holes will increase the sensitivity at the expense of definition, and vice versa. In practice, a number of different collimators are used, depending on whether sensitivity or definition is the most important parameter in a particular study.

It should be noted that the thickness of the lead must be matched to the energy of the gamma rays from the radionuclide being used. If the lead forming the septa is too thick the camera's sensitivity will be drastically reduced; if it is not thick enough some gamma rays from other non-specific directions will penetrate the collimator and be absorbed in the crystal, degrading the image.

The gamma camera only works well within a relatively narrow range of gamma-ray energy. If that energy is too high a large proportion of the gamma rays pass right through the camera's crystal without being absorbed by it. This reduces the sensitivity of the gamma camera and other collimators with thicker lead septa must be used to absorb the non-orthogonal radiation, further reducing both sensitivity and camera resolution. On the other hand, if the gamma-ray energy is too low, many of the gamma rays are scattered or

absorbed within the patient, reducing image quality and increasing the radiation dose to the patient.

The usefulness of the gamma camera also relies on its ability to register equal amounts of radiation anywhere within its field of view as being equal. This ability (or lack of it!) is known as the **field uniformity**. The task of keeping a detector composed of a large scintillation crystal, many tens of PM-tubes and complex positional electronics stable is by no means straightforward. In a modern gamma camera good field uniformity is achieved by a combination of high quality components and in-built correction circuitry.

The gamma camera 'head', consisting of the removable collimator, crystal, PM-tubes, and at least some preamplification circuitry, is housed within a lead bowl to exclude stray radiation. The whole 'head', weighing perhaps 500 kg, needs to be moveable to any position over, under or near a patient with great precision, and to be lockable in that position.

The other circuitry necessary to run the gamma camera, together with the display and any photographic devices, are usually found in a separate console. These photographic or 'hard-copy' devices must allow images to be taken either for fixed times or for fixed counts, and in a variety of different image formats so that multiple images may be recorded on one piece of film.

As with the rectilinear scanner, the quality of a gamma camera image will be critically dependent on the number of counts that have been detected to form the image. For any given collimator and gamma camera system, the only way this number of counts can be increased is to either administer a greater activity to the patient or to increase the imaging time.

Taking the former course might lead to unaccept-able radiation doses to the patient, and thus the activities that can be administered are strictly controlled. In practice, gamma camera images usually contain of the order of 500 000 counts, acquired over 100–200 s. This allows the radiation doses received by the patient to be of the same order as for other radiation-based investigations, such as those using X-ray techniques.

The improvement in image quality and resolution between the rectilinear scanner and the gamma camera is readily visible by comparing the images of Figures 12.1(b) and 12.5, from the same administered activity. For this reason the gamma camera has almost completely superceded the rectilinear scanner.

Taking images with the gamma camera in this way certainly overcomes one of the disadvantages of the rectilinear scanner – that of building up the imaged area piece by piece. It also allows the possibility of taking a sequence of gamma camera images to follow a dynamic process.

(a)

(b)

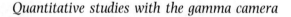

Figure 12.5   Images of the skeleton from a gamma camera ((b) shows an image from a patient with secondary bone cancer)

Quantitative studies with the gamma camera

The radionuclide imaging techniques so far discussed have lost the quantitative aspect of the use of radionuclides – the result is images rather than numbers. This potential disadvantage of radionuclide imaging studies has been overcome by linking an imaging computer to the gamma camera.

Data acquisition and processing

Data from the gamma camera is fed through a device known as an analogue-to-digital converter (ADC). This, as its name suggests, converts the continuously varying **analogue** X- and Y-signals from the gamma camera into discrete **digital**

values that can be stored in a computer. After the data have been collected into the computer, they can be used to create an image by telling a visual display unit (VDU) to display the number of counts at each memory location as the brightness (or colour) of a particular point on the screen.

The 'graininess' of the computer image can be altered by using more or fewer memory locations to display the gamma camera's field of view. The number of picture elements, or **pixels** as they are known, that are used for an image depends only on the size of the computer's memory. Typical radionuclide images use a matrix of 64×64, 128×128 or 256×256 pixels. The use of much greater numbers of pixels per image does not result in better quality images, as they will have exceeded the resolution limit of the gamma camera.

The great advantage of using an image processor to store the number and location of the acquired counts is that there is now quantitative information again, as well as an image. With the data stored within the computer it is also possible to manipulate the way that data is displayed, for example to improve the contrast of the image.

The computer is sometimes used to store a sequence of images to follow a dynamic process, such as the accumulation and excretion of a particular tracer through the kidneys. One option is then to allow the data to be run (and re-run) as a cine-type image sequence. From the same data it is also possible to select the same group of pixels within each image of the sequence and examine how the counts in those pixels vary throughout the sequence.

This variation can be graphically displayed, as in Figure 12.6, or can be used to create numerical indices related to the function of the part of the body under investigation. It is in this regard that radionuclide imaging techniques differ so greatly from X-ray imaging techniques.

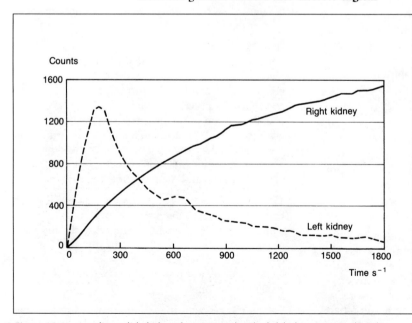

Figure 12.6   A radionuclide kidney function study. The left kidney is normal, with a rapid uptake and clearance of the tracer. The right kidney, which has its outflow blocked by a kidney stone, demonstrates this with a curve that shows a gradual uptake but no clearance. If the stone were not removed the kidney would eventually be irreparably damaged.

X-ray images are largely anatomical, with fine resolution of the body's structures. By comparison, radionuclide images are much cruder in terms of the detail they present, but provide information primarily about the physiology, the *function*, of the area under investigation. The exact nature of that information depends on the type of tracer used for the studies.

Radionuclides and radiopharmaceuticals

^{99m}Technetium

The radionuclide ^{99m}technetium (^{99m}Tc), particularly when chemically 'labelled' to other physiologically useful molecules, accounts for most diagnostic administrations. There are excellent reasons for this, connected with its radioactive properties.

(a) It has a physical half-life of 6 hours, which is long enough for tracers incorporating it to reach the organ to be imaged, but not too long to cause unnecessary irradiation of the patient after the test has been completed.

(b) The 'm' in '99m' means that it decays from a metastable or excited state, and thus emits only gamma rays. The lack of beta-particle emissions, which would be absorbed within the body and contribute nothing to the image, reduces the radiation dose received by the patient. This in turn allows the use of slightly larger administered doses than would be possible with

other radionuclides, producing better quality images.

(c) It has a gamma-ray energy of 140 keV, which is well matched to the optimum imaging performance of the gamma camera.

However, the 6-hour half-life of ^{99m}Tc which is so physiologically advantageous could in itself create a problem, as it would be necessary to transport large activities on virtually a daily basis to all those centres performing nuclear medicine studies. The solution to this potential problem is the so-called ^{99m}Tc 'generator'.

The ^{99m}technetium 'generator'

A photograph and schematic cut-away diagram of a typical ^{99m}technetium generator are shown in Figure 12.7.

The core of the generator is a small alumina column onto which is adsorbed between 2 and 20 GBq ($2-20 \times 10^9$ Bq) of ^{99}molybdenum as ammonium molybdate. Surrounding the column is lead shielding to reduce the gamma-ray dose rate external to the generator from such a large activity. The ^{99}molybdenum gradually decays (with a half-life of 67 hours) to ^{99m}technetium, which is then present on the column as a pertechnetate ion (TcO_4)⁻.

When required, an evacuated glass vial with a rubber seal is placed on a needle at the top of the generator. This draws sterile saline solution from a

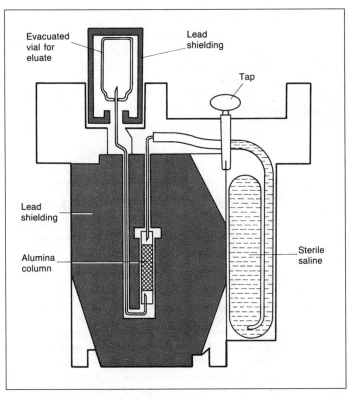

Figure 12.7 ^{99m}Technetium 'generator'

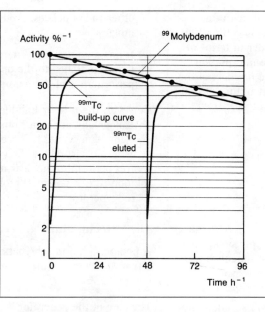

Figure 12.8   Dynamic equilibrium in the ⁹⁹ᵐtechnetium 'generator'

plastic bag through the column. As it passes through the column the chloride ions in the saline exchange with the pertechnetate ions but not the bound molybdate ions. What emerges into the vial is therefore a solution of sodium pertechnetate, $Na^+(^{99m}TcO_4)^-$, in saline.

This can then be diluted and divided into a number of individual patient 'doses'. These are used in imaging studies when compounded into radiopharmaceuticals, as described below.

Having been **eluted**, as the process is called, the concentration of ⁹⁹ᵐtechnetium within the generator falls to zero. Gradually, however, more of the ⁹⁹molybdenum decays once again and within approximately 24 hours has again reached dynamic equilibrium, Figure 12.8.

The generator works because the 67-hour half-life of ⁹⁹molybdenum allows a daily elution to take place until the radioactive concentration falls to too low a level for useful solutions of ⁹⁹ᵐtechnetium to be produced. This usually happens after approximately 2 half-lives of the parent ⁹⁹molybdenum, or approximately 6 days.

Thus a weekly delivery of a ⁹⁹molybdenum–⁹⁹ᵐtechnetium generator allows a nuclear medicine department to produce ⁹⁹ᵐtechnetium 'on-tap', at least on a daily basis.

From radionuclide to radiopharmaceutical

In most cases the ⁹⁹ᵐtechnetium must be **labelled** chemically to another compound which carries the radionuclide to the specific locations that are under investigation. These labelled compounds, or **radiopharmaceuticals** as they are known, are the products of careful work by radiochemists and radiopharmacists.

The work must indeed be careful, for the end-product must be sterile, non-toxic, a suitable pH for

the body's requirements, and chemically pure to allow the imaging of a specific function.

Because of the large demand for such radiopharmaceuticals worldwide, the most commonly used compounds are now mass produced and freeze-dried. They can then be re-constituted with the radionuclide of choice on-site and subsequently administered to the patient.

Examples of compounds used with ⁹⁹ᵐtechnetium given in Table 12.1.

Table 12.1

Compound	'Active' component	Imaging study
methylene diphosphonate (MDP)	phosphate	bone
macro-aggregated albumin (MAA)	aggregates	lung
tin colloid	colloid	liver
mercapto acetyl triglycine (MAG3)	whole molecule	kidney

So far it will be noticed that ⁹⁹ᵐtechnetium has been discussed exclusively, but a number of other radionuclides are also used, usually compounded in a similar way. However, there are a few radionuclides that are used in the form in which they are produced. One example of such a radionuclide is the radioactive gas ¹³³xenon used in lung function studies.

Nuclear reactors

Most radionuclides used in imaging studies are produced in nuclear reactors. A sample of a pure nuclide is placed inside the reactor core using a remote handling device. The high neutron flux within the reactor then causes nuclear reactions to take place within the sample. The most common reaction involves the capture of slow neutrons by nuclei of the sample.

Typical reactions are:

⁹⁸molybdenum → ⁹⁹molybdenum
                          (→ ⁹⁹ᵐtechnetium)

¹³⁰tellurium → ¹³¹tellurium   (→ ¹³¹iodine)

³¹phosphorus → ³²phosphorus

Sometimes the slow neutrons are used to produce controlled fission within a sample of ²³⁵uranium itself. This results in the production of a number of radionuclides, amongst which are ⁹⁹molybdenum and ¹³¹iodine.

Other, though less common, reactions use fast neutrons within the reactor. One reaction uses a sample of ¹⁴nitrogen, which when irradiated with fast neutrons captures the neutrons and emits protons, producing the radionuclide ¹⁴carbon. This particular radionuclide is used extensively for labelling organic molecules in biological and medical research.

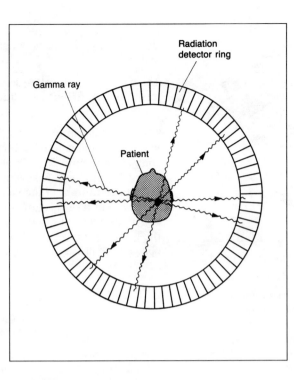

Figure 12.9
PET scanner

of the radioactive gas ^{127}xenon, used in lung imaging studies.

Radionuclide tomography

One extension to the use of radionuclide imaging techniques is in the acquisition and display of **tomographic**, or three-dimensional, information. The use of depth information in tomographic radionuclide images provides greater contrast between the various structures in the body than in standard **planar** imaging, but at the expense of image detail. This is because the complex mathematical processes involved in the reconstruction of the images degrade the information present in those images, and increase the 'noise' present.

Radionuclide tomography is usually done in one of two ways, as described below.

Positron emission tomography

Positron emission tomography (**PET**) does not use a gamma camera, but has an imaging device usually composed of a ring of small scintillation detectors around the patient, Figure 12.9. It uses the phenomenon of positron-electron annihilation, where a positron and an electron combine to produce two gamma rays, each of energy 511 keV. These travel in opposite directions from the site of the annihilation.

The coincidental detection of the two gamma rays tells an imaging computer connected to the detectors that an annihilation event has occurred somewhere on a line joining the two detectors. Multiple such coincidences enable the computer to reconstruct images of the distribution of the positron-emitting radionuclides within the detector area.

Such machines, known as PET scanners, are very costly because of the complex technology involved in their construction. They have nevertheless found a significant role, particularly in research applications. This role has emerged because of radionculides such as ^{15}oxygen and ^{18}fluorine. These radionuclides are incorporated into compounds which are then used to image oxygen and glucose utilisation, and have provided detailed images of the brain's physiology in various disease states.

Single-photon tomography

Single-photon tomography is so called because it uses the single gamma-ray photons from radionuclides such as ^{99m}technetium, as opposed to the two photons produced in positron decay.

Although some manufacturers have produced specific instruments with rings of detectors like the PET scanners, most single-photon tomography is

Particle accelerators

The production of certain radionuclides can only be achieved using high-energy nuclear reactions, and thus cannot be done within a nuclear reactor. Under these circumstances the radionuclides are obtained using particle accelerators. The most common type of accelerator used for this purpose is the **cyclotron**.

The cyclotron accelerates a beam of charged particles to bombard a 'target' of a particular, high-purity nuclide. Over a period of time the nuclear reactions arising from this bombardment transmute the target material into a different, radioactive nuclide.

Various charged particles can be used in different nuclear reactions to produce a wide range of radionuclides. One example bombards a target of ^{121}antimony with alpha particles, producing the radionuclide ^{123}iodine which is used in thyroid and other studies. Another reaction bombards ^{17}nitrogen with deuterons to produce the positron (positively charged electron)-emitting radionuclide ^{15}oxygen.

Some radionuclides require still higher-energy reactions than can be produced in most commercial cyclotrons. In these cases a **linear accelerator** such as the one at Brookhaven in the USA is used. This can accelerate protons to over 200 MeV, and with this level of energy a number of more complex reactions are possible.

One example uses a target of ^{133}caesium, bombarded with the high-energy protons. A single proton of the required energy striking the caesium nucleus causes two protons and five neutrons to be dislodged from that nucleus. This creates an atom

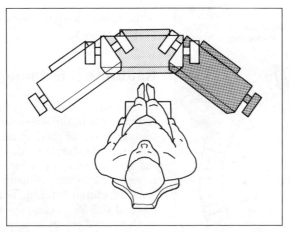

Figure 12.10
Single-photon
tomography

carried out using gamma cameras, as Figure 12.10 shows.

The gamma camera takes a series of images (typically 64) at fixed angles around the patient. The whole sequence is stored on the gamma camera's computer and reconstructed to give images of the distribution of the tracer as 'slices' through the patient in any chosen direction, similar to the process used in X-ray CT imaging (Chapter 11). Single-photon tomography has found its greatest usage in cerebral blood flow and cardiac imaging studies. These more sophisticated applications are relatively recent developments, and are gradually finding their way into routine imaging practice.

Case study

A 77-year-old woman had been admitted to hospital to have a hip replacement operation. The operation proceeded smoothly and successfully, but several days after the operation she began to develop a fluid swelling in the legs, and a feeling of breathlessness.

Under these circumstances, the clinical suspicion was that the patient had developed a condition known as pulmonary embolism – blood clots which had formed in the veins of the legs, then travelled up the major veins and into the lungs, where they became trapped.

Untreated, the patient could easily die as clots progressively block more of the lungs' vessels. The treatment for this condition consists of infusions of the drug heparin, which 'thins' the blood, breaking up the clots. However, this in turn can be dangerous, as it makes the patient susceptible to uncontrolled bleeding. The treatment is therefore not used unless the diagnosis has a high degree of certainty.

A chest X-ray was first performed, but showed no abnormality. This did not exclude the possibility of pulmonary embolism, however, as the X-ray only shows positive when the lungs are severely damaged.

The patient was therefore sent to the nuclear medicine department for a lung ventilation and perfusion study.

This study was in two parts. In the morning, she was asked to breath for 2 minutes an aerosol containing around 20 MBq of a compound labelled with ^{99m}technetium. Following the inhalation, she was seated in front of the gamma camera and six images were taken, Figure 12.11. The images were taken posteriorly (from the back), anteriorly (from the front), laterally (from each side), and posterior obliquely (half-way between posterior and lateral).

The posterior image was acquired first, with the image containing around 200 000 counts over 5 minutes. The other five images were then acquired for the same length of time as the posterior, to give images of comparable film density.

The patient was then allowed to rest for around 4 hours, to give time for the aerosol to be cleared from the lungs by the natural breakdown processes.

80 MBq of the radiopharmaceutical ^{99m}Tc-MAA was then injected through a vein in the arm. This radiopharmaceutical consists of fine aggregates of particles which are easily trapped in the lungs. Again, a series of six images were taken, this time containing 400 000 counts in the posterior image (the higher administered activity allowed more counts to be collected in the same or shorter time, giving higher-quality images).

The theory behind the test is that the aerosol **ventilation** images, obtained through inhalation of the tracer, show the function of the airways, whereas the MAA **perfusion** images show the lungs' blood flow. Any area of reduced uptake which only appears on the perfusion image therefore shows a defect only of the blood supply. This is highly likely to be due to a blood clot – pulmonary embolism. Areas which show reduced uptake in both sets of images are more likely to be due to infection or chronic lung problems which have affected both the air and blood flow within the lungs.

The images in Figure 12.11 show large defects in the middle and upper parts of the right lung, and smaller defects in the left lung – but only on the perfusion images.

This therefore confirmed the diagnosis of pulmonary embolism, and the need to start the heparin treatment immediately. This was done, and the patient went on to make a full recovery.

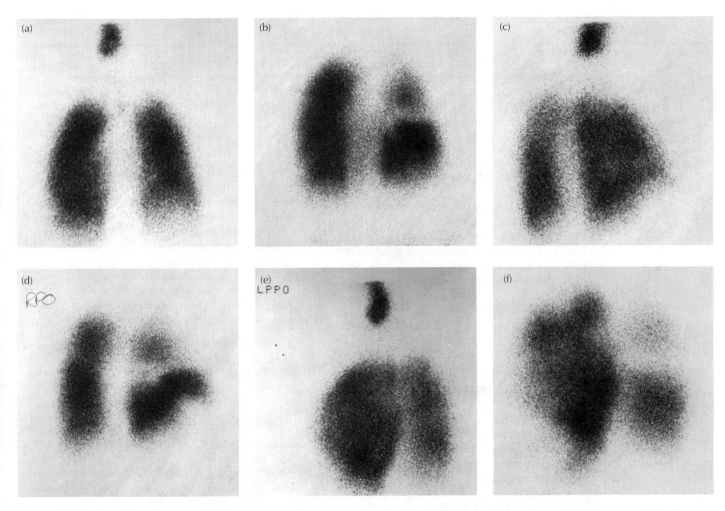

Figure 12.11   (a) and (b) show the posterior ventilation (air flow) and perfusion (blood flow) images. The left lung is on the left of the image. (c) and (d) show the right posterior oblique ventilation and perfusion images. The images mainly show the right lung, although part of the left lung can also be seen.

(e) and (f) show the left posterior oblique ventilation and perfusion images. These images mainly show the left lung.
Images show a large area of virtually absent perfusion through the middle part of the right lung, and reduced perfusion in the upper part of the same lung. Patchy perfusion is also seen at the base of, and towards the top of, the left lung on the left posterior oblique image.

Questions

1. a) State *three* factors which are important in choosing a suitable radionuclide for nuclear imaging of particular parts of the body. Name *one* radionuclide in common use for this purpose.

    b) Draw a labelled sketch of the main component parts of a gamma camera. Explain how it can be used with a radionuclide to obtain the desired image of a particular part of the body.

    c) Explain how information obtained from such an image differs from that obtained from a diagnostic X-ray image.

(JMB)

13 ULTRASOUND

Ultrasound in medicine

Medical ultrasound is one of the fastest growing imaging techniques in medicine today. Although the imaging of foetuses in the womb is probably the best known use of ultrasound, it is also used to image many other organs and to map the flow of blood through the blood vessels and the heart. Ultrasound is also used as a therapy for speeding the repair of damaged tissue. Alternatively, ultrasound can be used at much higher power levels to smash kidney stones, thus avoiding the use of surgery on patients.

Ultrasound waves

Ultrasound waves, like sound waves, are pressure waves which have a constant velocity c in a particular medium. The wave velocity c is related to the distance s travelled by the wave in time t by the usual formula

$$c = s / t$$

Turning this equation on its head, the distance s travelled by a wave in time t is given by:

$$s = c t$$

This relationship between distance and time gives rise to a method known as the **pulse–echo** technique which is used to produce an ultrasound image. This technique relies on knowing the speed of sound in a given medium. If a short pulse of sound travels to an object as shown in Figure 13.1, is reflected back and the time between emission of the pulse and detection of its echo is recorded, then the distance of the object from the machine can be calculated – it is half the product of the time taken and the velocity of the sound.

This simple technique is the main principle of ultrasound imaging. To understand how ultrasound images are produced in practice we must consider properties of ultrasound waves in more detail.

Properties of ultrasound waves

Ultrasonic waves share the same basic properties as audible sound waves. Both sound and ultrasound waves consist of longitudinal pressure waves in the medium through which they are being transmitted. Without that medium neither sound nor ultrasound can be transmitted. The major difference between the two is in the frequency of the waves. Whereas sound waves are in the frequency range 20 Hz–20 kHz, ultrasound waves have frequencies in the range 20 kHz–20 MHz.

The frequency of the ultrasound remains constant as the wave passes through different media and for this reason the wave is characterised by the frequency. The wave velocity c and wavelength λ vary for different materials.

$$c = f \lambda$$

The wave velocity c is dependent on the elasticity K of the medium and the density d such that:

$$c = \sqrt{(K/d)}$$

The characteristic acoustic impedance Z of a medium is given by:

$$Z = dc$$

The energy from the vibrating body which is the source of the ultrasound is carried in the medium by the pressure fluctuations at each point. As the amplitude of the pressure wave becomes larger, the energy carried becomes greater. The energy flow varies with both position and time. The energy flow is therefore best described in terms of the intensity at a particular point in space and time. For

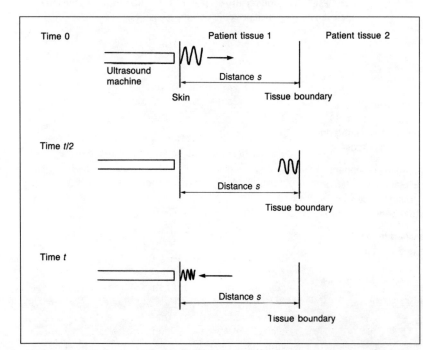

Figure 13.1   The principle of the pulse–echo technique

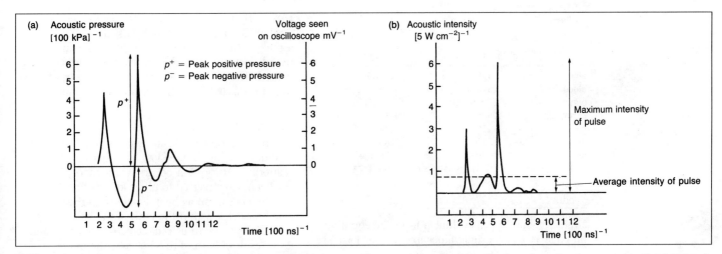

Figure 13.2 (a) The variation of pressure at a point in space in an ultrasound beam as time varies. Note that the voltage signal generated by the detector has the same shape as the acoustic pressure signal. (b) The corresponding changes in intensity (proportional to p^2) at the same point

practical purposes here the intensity considered is the average over time. Intensity is defined as the rate of flow of energy through an area of one square metre or one square centimetre in an imaginary plane at right angles to the direction of wave motion. The units of intensity are watts per square metre (W m^{-2}). However, these units are found to be too large in practice and so smaller units of W cm^{-2} and even mW cm^{-2} are used.

It is important to realise that the intensity I and the pressure p at a point in an ultrasound beam are related by the equation:

$$I = \frac{p^2}{2dc}$$

Although intensity is important in the theory, in practice it is the pressure which is used to detect the ultrasound beam. Figure 13.2 demonstrates the relation between (a) the pressure, and (b) the

intensity changes with time for a point in a medium experiencing the passage of an ultrasound pulse.

Refraction and reflection of ultrasound waves at boundaries – echoes

When an ultrasound wave meets the boundary between two media, it undergoes reflection and refraction in a similar way to light and sound waves.

For the case of refraction (see Figure 13.3):

$$\frac{\sin \theta_i}{\sin \theta_t} = \frac{c_1}{c_2}$$

Whereas for light it is the refractive index which determines the ratio of the velocities in two media, for sound it is the acoustic impedance which determines this ratio. The acoustic impedance Z of a medium is given by the formula:

$$Z = dc$$

Refraction at a boundary diverts some of the wave out of the beam and is one cause of attenuation of the beam.

For the case of reflection, which is our main concern here, it can be shown that for normal incidence the reflected intensity I_r when sound of intensity I_i is incident at the boundary of two media of acoustic impedance Z_1 and Z_2 is given by:

$$\frac{I_r}{I_i} = \left[\frac{Z_2 - Z_1}{Z_2 + Z_1}\right]^2$$

This equation shows that the relative values of acoustic impedance of the two media at a boundary determine how much of the wave is reflected. Table 13.1 shows typical values of acoustic impedance Z for some tissues. From these values intensities of reflected relative to incident intensities can be evaluated.

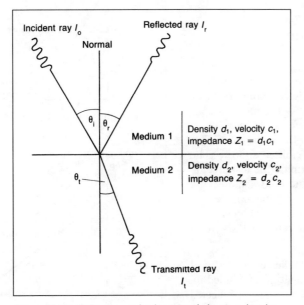

Figure 13.3 Reflection and refraction of ultrasound at the boundary between two tissues, 1 and 2

Table 13.1

Medium	Propagation velocity c	Characteristic impedance Z
	m s⁻¹	10⁶ kg m⁻² s⁻¹
air	330	0.0004
blood	1570	1.59
bone	2700–4100	3.75–7.38
castor oil	1500	1.4
fat	1450	1.38
liver	1550	1.65
lung	650–1160	0.26–0.46
muscle	1545–1630	1.65–1.74
perspex	2680	3.2
water	1480	1.52

Typical values of I_r/I_i evaluated from the equation on page 107 and using values from Table 13.1 are:

~0.9994	for an air/fat interface
~2×10^{-4}	for liver/muscle interface
~1×10^{-2}	for fat/lean muscle interface
~0.18	for muscle/bone interface

In other words at a muscle/bone interface, the acoustic impedance of the bone is 3–5 times larger than that of the muscle and so 25–45% of the incident ultrasound is reflected – there is a strong reflection. At a muscle/fat interface about 1% of the incident ultrasound is reflected. At an air/fat interface over 99% of the incident intensity is reflected. In fact there is nearly total reflection at any air/soft-tissue interface, so that a beam of ultrasound is not transmitted through air to the body. For this reason air must be excluded from a transducer/body surface interface if structures below the surface are to be seen. This is usually done by using a gel with an impedance close to that of soft tissue. This effect also means that areas behind the air cavities within the body (for instance the lungs) cannot be seen, and that bony structures cannot be imaged except in surface outline.

Ultrasound scanning and the pulse–echo technique

The reflection of a beam of pulses of ultrasound by different tissue boundaries within the body is the basis of ultrasound scanning. Each boundary in the path of the beam reflects some of the incident beam back to the transducer. In other words each boundary returns an 'echo' to the transducer. The time between the pulse being emitted and the echo being received is used to determine the distance of the boundary from the transducer. In addition, the intensity of the echo is used to distinguish the different tissue boundaries. Many of the techniques of ultrasound scanning are the same as those used in the field of radar.

The range of intensities of the reflected waves, and the corresponding range of amplitudes recorded in ultrasound machines, is large. The largest reflected intensity is tens of thousands times the weakest. This range of intensities is known as the **dynamic range**. Dynamic range was also mentioned in Chapter 3, page 19, when discussing sound. Again, a scale with equal divisions of intensity is not useful. Instead a logarithmic scale, the decibel scale, is used. The decibel scale was mentioned in Chapter 3 and is discussed further in the next section.

Attenuation

When an ultrasound beam is propagated through a medium, energy may be lost by either absorption or scattering. Absorption occurs when energy from the beam is converted to other forms of energy, usually ending up as heat. Scattering arises because small particles within the path of the beam cause part of the wave to be redirected out of the beam. As a result of both of these effects, the initial intensity of a wave I_o is reduced by a constant factor μ (which is called the **attenuation factor**) when the beam has travelled through a distance s in the medium. When the beam travels a further distance s the intensity is reduced by μ again. Figure 13.4(a) shows the change of intensity of the wave with distance s. The distance h on the s-axis corresponds to the distance in which the intensity is halved, and is known as the half-value thickness. It can be shown that the intensity I_s of the wave after travelling a distance s in the medium is described by the equation:

$$I_s = I_o \exp(-\mu s)$$

The plot of the change of intensity with distance is an exponential curve, as shown in Figure 13.4(a).

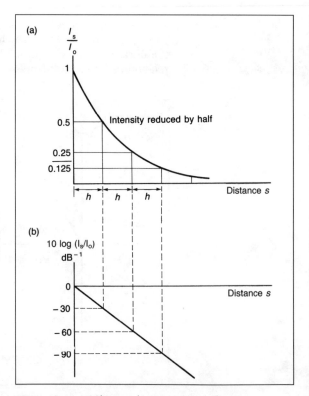

Figure 13.4 (a) Change of intensity I_s with distance s (b) Use of the logarithmic (decibel) scale

If the equation can be rewritten as:

$$\frac{I_s}{I_o} = \exp(-\mu s)$$

and then the natural log of each side taken:

$$\ln \frac{I_s}{I_o} = -\mu s$$

But:

$$\ln \frac{I_s}{I_o} = \frac{1}{2.3} \log_{10} \frac{I_s}{I_o}$$

if logarithms to the base ten are taken.

If $\log (I_s/I_o)$ is plotted against s, the graph will be a straight line of gradient -2.3μ as shown in Figure 13.4(b). The scale of the y-axis is a logarithmic scale and the units are multiplied by 10 to convert from the bel to the decibel scale. The decibel scale is discussed further in the next section. The coefficient of attenuation μ is expressed as dB cm^{-1}.

The decibel scale

Because of the large dynamic range of the reflected intensities, and because of the logarithmic attenuation of the intensity in a medium, it is more convenient to use a logarithmic scale of intensity level, just as was the case for sound in Chapter 3.

Referring to Chapter 3, but using the intensity of ultrasound, it can be shown that in a logarithmic scale the unit of intensity is the bel, which is defined such that for a detected beam of intensity I_d from original beam intensity of I_o:

Intensity level of the detected beam $= \log_{10} \dfrac{I_d}{I_o}$ bel

In practice the bel is too large a unit to be useful and the decibel or dB is used, where 1 bel = 10 dB.

Hence:

Intensity level of the detected beam $= 10 \times \log_{10} \dfrac{I_d}{I_o}$ dB

So, if the intensity of the ultrasound is reduced from I_o to $I_o/2000$, then:

New intensity level $= 10 \times \log_{10} \dfrac{I_o}{2000 \, I_o}$

$= -100 \times \log_{10}(20) + 10 \times \log_{10}(1)$

Thus the change in intensity level $= -100 \times \log_{10}(20)$ dB

$= -100 \times 1.30$ dB

$= -130$ dB

The minus sign indicates that the detected intensity level is below the initial intensity level.

The intensity level of a detected beam of ultrasound in an abdominal scan may be 70 dB below the original intensity level emitted from the machine.

The attenuation coefficient μ is dependent on the frequency of the ultrasound beam such that attenuation increases with increasing frequency. This means that organs deep within the body such as the heart or liver will only be penetrated by ultrasound frequencies of up to 3.5 MHz, whereas those such as the thyroid or breast can be penetrated by frequencies of 7 or 10 MHz. Table 13.2 shows some attenuation coefficients at 1 MHz for some common materials.

Table 13.2

Medium	Attenuation coefficient at 1 MHz, μ dB^{-1} cm
air	10
blood	0.2
bone	3–10
castor oil	1
fat	0.63
liver	1.3
lung	40
muscle	1.5–2.5
perspex	2
water	0.002
soft tissue	1.0

Production of ultrasound waves

Ultrasound waves are produced by a vibrating body, the most common being a piezoelectric crystal. This type of crystal has the property of being mechanically distorted when a potential difference is applied across its body. Conversely, when the piezoelectric crystal is mechanically distorted, a potential difference is created across it, as seen in Chapter 5. In this way these crystals can be used as both sources and detectors of ultrasound waves. A common piezoelectric source is quartz, but most early ultrasound transducers used the synthetic ceramic lead zirconate titanate. Today polyvinylidine difluoride (PVDF) is more commonly used.

When the frequency of the electronic signal is the same as the natural frequency of the crystal, the amplitude of the mechanical vibration of the crystal is a maximum and is known as the **resonant frequency**. This frequency is used in ultrasound probes to give the maximum amplitude of ultrasound wave for the minimum input of electrical energy. The resonant frequency of the crystal is determined by its geometric dimensions. Diagnostic ultrasound probes have frequencies in the range 0.75–10 MHz.

Figure 13.5 shows a piezoelectric element electrically coupled between the two terminals of a voltage source. Applying an a.c. signal of several hundred volts across the element will distort it by about 0.1% at the resonant frequency. If the resonant frequency is 5 MHz then the dimensions of the crystal will change at that rate and a 5 MHz

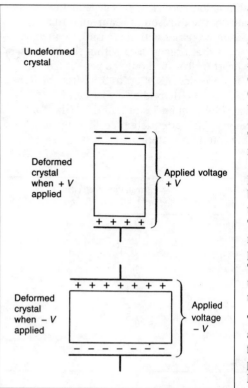

Figure 13.5   Deformation of a piezoelectric crystal by application of a potential between two plates at opposite ends of the crystal

ultrasound signal will be transmitted into the adjacent medium.

Figure 13.6(a) shows the construction of a simple device to produce ultrasound which is known as a disc piston-type source. The disc of piezoelectric material is typically 10–20 mm in diameter. Behind the crystal is a backing block which damps the response of the crystal. The device is the simplest of many different kinds used to produce ultrasound beams. They are all called ultrasonic or electroacoustic transducers or probes.

The above method produces a long ultrasound pulse. In fact only a short ultrasound pulse is desired (see below). In theory this could be achieved by switching on the a.c. signal for a short period of time, then switching it off, as shown in Figure 13.6(b). In practice, the short pulse is produced by discharging a capacitor through a resonant circuit, Figure 13.6(c). Even so, this still produces rather a long pulse. To shorten the period of the ultrasound pulse a backing material is attached to the crystal. This damps the pulse in the

same way as a hand on a gong shortens the time for which the gong rings.

Short pulses typically of one microsecond duration are generated as was shown in Figure 13.2(a).

The pulses are sent into the medium and the returning echoes are detected by the transducer, amplified and recorded in the ultrasound machine.

In general the higher the frequency, the smaller the wavelength and the better the resolution gained in diagnostic techniques. This means that finer detail can be seen in images when higher frequencies are used. You would therefore expect that the highest possible frequencies would be used.

Unfortunately, the higher the frequency, the greater is the attenuation of the beam. The net result of this is that investigations near the surface (thyroid, testicular and mammography scans) all use a high frequency probe of, say, 7 or 10 MHz, and fine detail will be seen in these scans. Investigations of deeper tissues require a lower frequency probe, with 3.5 MHz and 5 MHz being common, and less detailed structure can be seen in these scans.

Ultrasound beam shape

The simplest source of ultrasound is a disc-shaped piston which vibrates, as shown in Figure 13.6(a).

If a disc piston-type source of ultrasound has a piston head of radius a and moves sinusoidally with a wavelength l the beam shape is as shown in Figure 13.7(a).

The width of the beam depends on the diameter of the source and the distance from the source.

If four disc crystals are mounted on a rotating scan head, pulses are sent out along paths at different angles. A path is swept out in the shape of a wedge or sector.

For a linear array where there are many small crystals, the field is as shown in Figure 13.7(b).

The resolution of the ultrasound scanner is determined in the axial direction (the direction of the wave) by the pulse length, and in the transverse directions by the beam width. Usually the axial direction has a better resolution (~ 1 mm) than the transverse directions (~ 3–5 mm).

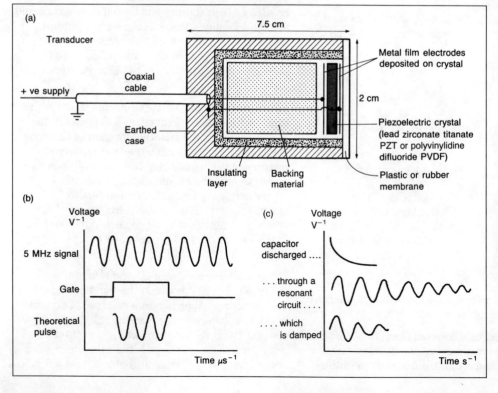

Figure 13.6
(a) Disc piston-type ultrasound source
(b) Theory   (c) Practice

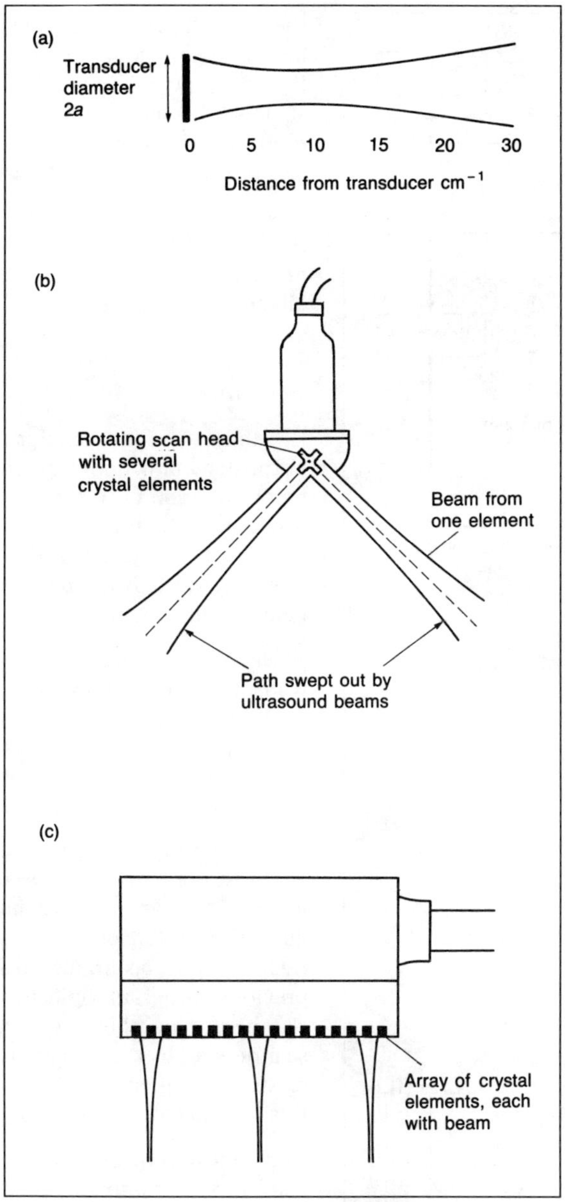

Figure 13.7
(a) The shape of the ultrasound beam
(b) A mechanical sector ultrasound transducer for B-scanning
(c) A linear array transducer for B-scanning

Linear arrays (Figure 13.7(c)) usually have a better transverse resolution than **sector scanners**. These two types of scanners are described in more detail on the next page.

Medical uses of ultrasound

Ultrasound is used as an imaging technique in medical diagnosis. Within the field of diagnostic imaging, ultrasound has four main scanning techniques, known as **A-scanning**, **B-scanning**, **M-scanning** and **Doppler-scanning**. It is usually only necessary to have one ultrasound machine and different probes can be used with it to produce the different techniques.

Ultrasound is also used in physiotherapy departments as a therapeutic technique in the management of tissue healing. The rate of healing

is said to be increased by the effects of local heating and large pressure changes which increase the blood flow to damaged tissues.

A further use of ultrasound is to be found in urology departments where it is used to break up kidney stones within the kidney. This technique is known as lithotripsy and it uses high output levels which are focused on the stones by a device called a **lithotripter**.

The two latter techniques are not discussed further here.

A-scanners

A-scanners were the first and the simplest of the ultrasound scanners and form the basis for the other scanners. Knowledge of how the A-scanner works is therefore useful in understanding ultrasound imaging techniques in general.

The A-scanner is made up of a transducer which acts as transmitter and receiver, an amplifier, a time-base generator and an oscilloscope. The output from the receiver is amplified and then connected to the Y-plates of the oscilloscope. The time-base is connected to the X-plates of the oscilloscope.

The start of each sweep of the oscilloscope is triggered by the time-base. At the same time an electronic pulse is generated and converted into an ultrasound pulse which enters the first medium. If the pulse encounters a tissue boundary a small proportion of the signal will be reflected back to the transducer.

When the reflected pulse reaches the transducer it will distort the crystal and result in a small potential difference across the crystal. This voltage signal is amplified and fed to the Y-plates of the oscilloscope. In this way a voltage spike is recorded on the oscilloscope.

The position of the spike on the X-axis is proportional to the time taken for the pulse to travel to the boundary and then back to the transducer. The amplitude of the signal is represented by the Y-axis deflection. The amplitude depends on the attenuation by the medium, the distance of the tissue boundary and the acoustic impedances of the two tissues at the boundaries.

If an ultrasound pulse is generated by a transducer at a given time into a body with four reflecting surfaces, at four later times echoes of the pulse will be detected by the transducer, Figure 13.8(a).

For soft tissue the wave velocity c of the ultrasound is approximately constant and taken to be 1540 m s^{-1}. Therefore for soft tissue boundaries the times t_s at which the echoes are received mainly depend on the distances s of the reflecting tissues below the surface of the body.

$$c = s/t$$

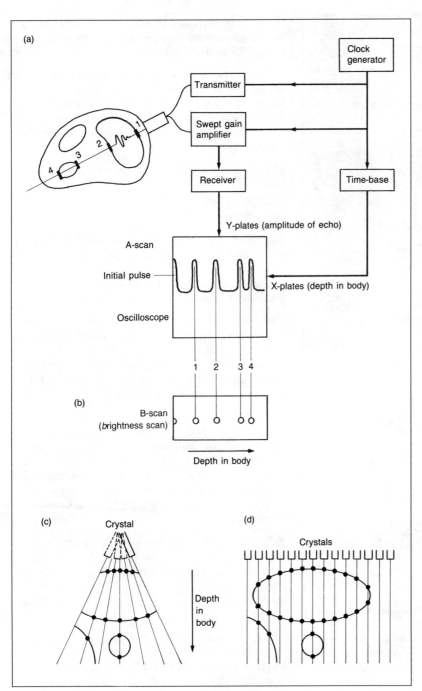

Figure 13.8 (a) The A-scanner (b) The one-dimensional B-scan
(c) A two-dimensional B-scan from the sector B-scanner. Lots of B-scans are taken one
after the other as the crystal is rotated. (d) A two-dimensional B-scan from the linear
array B-scanner. Each crystal is energised in turn.

the more distant boundaries will be weaker. This makes the image more difficult to interpret and so the later signals are amplified more than the near signals. This technique is known as **time-gain-compensation** or **TGC**. At the beginning of every session the operator will set up the TGC controls.

A-scanners are today used in the determination of the lens thickness and eye diameter before ophthalmic surgery. Reflections from only one direction can be observed at one time.

B-scanners

B-scanners use the same principle as A-scanners but instead of denoting the amplitude of the signal by the position on the Y-axis, the amplitude is denoted by the brightness of a spot on the trace, Figure 13.8(b). In addition B-scanners change the direction of the beam by various means so that a plane within the body is scanned.

Older machines relied on the operator moving a transducer in short sweeps whose positions were recorded by electromechanical means, in order to build up a B-scan picture. The image took some time to build up and was rather poor. Very few of these machines are in use today.

Today rotating sector and linear array probes are amongst many methods used to build up a B-scan image. These later models build up the picture almost instantaneously and so in the first years of their life were distinguished from the models in the previous paragraph by being called 'real-time scanners'. Now they are usually known just as B-scanners and so some confusion of terminology exists in the literature. The rate of development of this technology is outstripping the literature.

In a **sector scanner** the crystal inside the transducer is rotated by mechanical means through an arc of about 60 degrees, Figure 13.8(c). At several positions in the arc an ultrasound pulse is emitted and reflected back. Each time this happens one B-scan line of brightness dots is recorded by the scanner and is usually stored in a computer memory. By knowing the angle θ of each line and the position r of any dot within the line, the (X, Y) coordinate of that dot in the body can be computed. The Y-position on the screen indicates depth within the body whilst the X-position indicates the horizontal position. It is thus possible to build up an image of the tissue interfaces in a slice through the body which can be displayed on a TV monitor. Notice that only a 'wedge' or sector of the body can be imaged, as shown by Figure 13.8(c).

A **linear array probe** has many small crystals in a line. Each crystal emits pulses of ultrasound (usually in turn), and detects the echoes. Therefore each crystal produces one line of the B-scan. In this case the display is rectangular, Figure 13.8(d).

Each of the returning pulses causes distortion of the crystal and a resultant small change in electric potential across its opposite faces. The potential changes are amplified and recorded on an oscilloscope, with the Y-axis representing the voltage and the X-axis representing time. Four spikes will be observed on the trace. The X-axis can be calibrated in terms of distance instead of time if the speed of sound in the tissues is known.

As the pulse traverses the medium it is progressively attenuated, and so reflections from

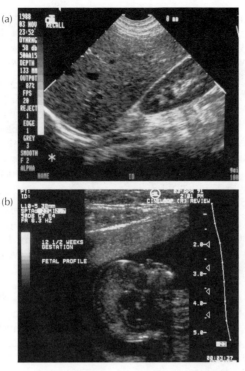

Figure 13.9   (a) Right kidney, artery and vein, taken with sector scanner (b) Foetal cheek, nose, lips and chin, taken with linear array

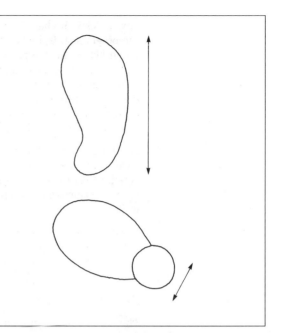

Figure 13.10   Dimensions of foetus used to predict birthdates   (a) Crown-rump length   (b) Biparietal diameter

Figure 13.9 shows the kinds of images produced by these probes.

The greatest use of B-scanning ultrasound machines is in obstetrics, where images of the developing foetus may be produced. Nearly every baby born today in the UK will have had an ultrasound scan when a foetus. The size of the foetal head and body will be measured at intervals during pregnancy.

The length of the body from crown to rump, as shown in Figure 13.10(a), is measured at 7–14 weeks. This is done by moving cursors under the control of a joystick so that they lie on either end of the image of the foetus. The machine then calculates the distance between the two points assuming a constant speed of sound.

This crown–rump measurement is used to estimate how long the pregnancy has lasted. This is done by using graphs, such as that shown in Figure 13.11(a), which are supplied with each machine. The graph shows the average size of a foetus for each week of pregnancy. This means that if the size of the foetus is known, the number of weeks into the pregnancy can be determined. The lines either side of each point on the graph show the possible error in the measurement, which is of the order of one week.

At about 18 weeks a more sensitive test of the length of the pregnancy is carried out by measuring the biparietal diameter, the widest diameter of the baby's head, Figure 13.10(b), and comparing this with a chart such as Figure 13.11(b).

These measurements are very important because forty per cent of mothers are not sure how long they have been pregnant, and it is crucial to know

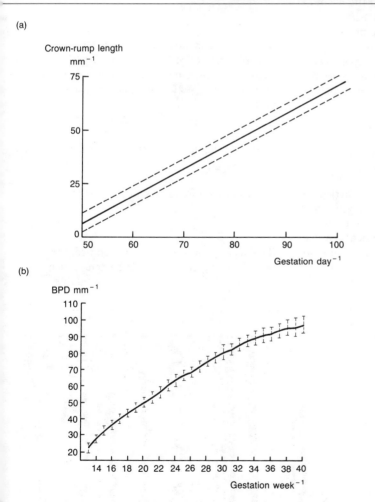

Figure 13.11   (a) Relation of foetal crown-rump length to age. About 95% of normal foetuses lie between the outer lines.   (b) Relation of foetal biparietal diameter to gestation. Again, about 95% of normal foetuses lie between the extremes plotted.

how quickly the baby is developing at each stage in the pregnancy. If the baby's growth slows down much below the average at any stage, the clinician will suspect that something is wrong. Perhaps for some reason the baby is being starved of food. If the baby's head is growing much faster than normal but the body is not, then it may be that the baby has 'water on the brain' or hydrocephaly.

Still later in the pregnancy the limbs and even facial features can be imaged in much greater detail, as Figure 13.9(b) shows, and this can be used to ensure that the pregnancy is proceeding well.

B-scanners are also commonly used to determine whether there are cysts or tumours in the liver, breast, thyroid or abdominal organs.

M-scanners

The 'M' stands for motion. In effect, an M-scanner records the changes in the one-dimensional B-scan over a period of time. The B-scan is made up of a line of hot bright spots at positions corresponding to the depth of the tissue interfaces in the beam at a particular period of time, Figure 13.12(a). Thermal paper is used, which has the property of turning black if heat is applied to its surface. As the thermal paper rolls past the hot bright spots, each forms a trace on the paper. If there is no movement of the tissue boundaries, then a series of straight lines is produced.

If the ultrasound is directed towards a moving boundary such as the foetal heart, a trace such as Figure 13.12(b) is produced, where the curved lines show the movement of the heart walls with time.

This technique is often used when a miscarriage is suspected in the early stages of pregnancy. Even at a few weeks, when the features of the embryo cannot be visualised on the scan, the heart can be seen beating. This reassures the doctor – and more importantly the mother – that the foetus is still alive.

The M-scanner is also used to monitor the function of different parts of the adult heart.

Doppler scanners

These scanners use the Doppler effect to determine the speed at which objects (usually blood corpuscles) are moving. Doppler techniques are used in assessing blood flow, especially within the heart valves, and the blood supply to the brain via the carotid arteries, and also in determining the blood flow to the foetus through the umbilical cord.

The simplest way to understand this is to consider a continuous ultrasound wave of frequency f and velocity c incident on a stationary boundary as depicted in Figure 13.13(a). If the boundary is stationary the wavelength l is given by:

$$l = c/f$$

The waves passing the transducer at O in one second are contained in a distance c. This is equivalent to a wave starting at A, being reflected at B and just reaching O, so that the distance travelled between A and O must be c. In this case:

$$c = AB + OB$$
$$= AO + 2OB$$

If the boundary now moves with a velocity v towards the transducer, FIgure 13.13(b), the waves from A are the same in number but are contained in a distance $c - 2v$. The apparent wavelength l' is given by:

$$l' = (c - 2v)/f$$

Therefore the apparent frequency f' is given by:

$$f' = cf/(c - 2v)$$

The change in frequency df is given by:

$$df = 2vf/(c - 2v)$$
$$\approx 2vf/c \text{ if } c \gg v$$

If the change in frequency is recorded, the velocity of the moving structure can be determined. The velocity can be either positive or negative

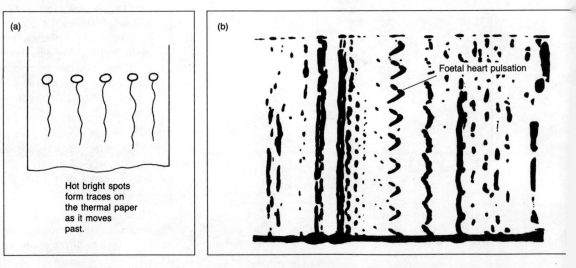

Figure 13.12
(a) The M-scan
(b) M-scan of foetal heart pulsation (Fh)

(a)

Hot bright spots form traces on the thermal paper as it moves past.

(b)

Foetal heart pulsation

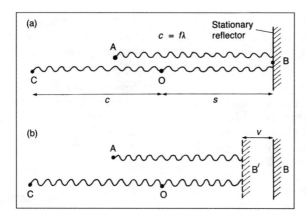

Figure 13.13
(a) Stationary reflector
(b) The Doppler effect seen when the reflector moves with velocity *v* towards the observer

depending on whether the movement is towards or away from the transducer. Figure 13.14 represents a Doppler scan trace caused by the movement of blood in the femoral artery. The vertical axis corresponds to frequency shift or velocity. Displacement above the axis denotes flow towards the observer, displacement below the axis away from the probe. The size of the displayed dot is proportional to the amplitude of the signal. The *x*-axis represents time. Note that at any time there is not just one frequency shift, but a range. The shape of the Doppler scan can tell the clinician much about the flow in an artery. The shape of the waveform indicates whether the blood flow is normal or damped by constrictions in the artery. The most common form of constriction is caused by plaque lining the vessel walls, more commonly known as hardening of the arteries.

In practice, continuous waves are not always used in Doppler machines. This is because continuous waves need an emitter of ultrasound and a separate detector. Instead pulses of ultrasound are used and the emitter and detector are the same.

Care must be taken to use the correct probe when using Doppler ultrasound near to the foetus. Pulsed Doppler can produce ultrasound waves with such very high intensity levels (even though for very short times) that it is just possible that damage to

the foetus could occur. For this reason continuous wave probes are used in measuring umbilical blood flow, or pulsed Doppler systems are used in obstetrics with intensities restricted to safe levels. It would not be wise to use probes designed for studies of the blood flow of the heart in studies in obstetrics.

Duplex scanners

Duplex scanners are a combination of real-time B-scanners and pulsed Doppler flowmeters. They allow a target (such as the heart or carotid artery) to be imaged on the screen using the B-scanner in the usual way, with the direction of the Doppler transducer superimposed on the image. The speed of the moving vessel is indicated on the screen. It is possible to change the direction and distance of the target so that the function of the different heart valves can be examined.

Colour doppler

When examining the blood flow through the heart, it is important to be able to determine the direction of the blood flow through the valves easily and quickly in order to be able to see if they are functioning correctly. The latest colour Doppler machines do this by displaying motion towards the transducer with one colour, say red, and motion away from the transducer by another colour, say blue.

The operator points the ultrasound probe towards a valve in the heart. The normal B-scan is displayed on the screen in black and white. In addition, if motion is detected at a point in the beam, it is displayed on the colour monitor as a dot of colour. If the motion is towards the transducer it is displayed as a red dot at the appropriate position on the screen. If the motion is away from the transducer it is displayed as a blue dot. As a normal valve opens, blood may move away from the transducer and a blue flash of colour will be superimposed on the valve. If the valve is not working normally the flow may not all be in one direction and some red may appear in the blue flash of colour. The cardiac technician can identify the function of the valves of the heart with colour Doppler in a fraction of the time that would have been necessary with black and white (monochrome) Doppler machines.

Colour Doppler is also used in examining carotid blood flow, where turbulence caused by the existence of sheets of plaque lining the artery walls interferes with the blood flow to the brain.

Hazards of ultrasound

The main effects of ultrasound on biological tissues are heating, and an effect called **cavitation** which is explained below.

The absorption of ultrasound by the tissues results in a heating of those tissues. The safe limit for

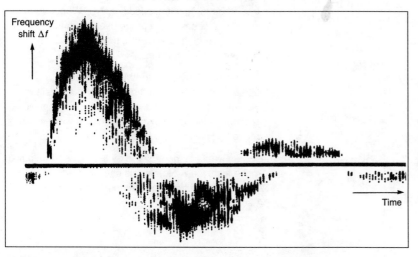

Figure 13.14　Doppler scan trace of blood flow in the femoral artery

thermal effects in diagnostic ultrasound is a temperature rise of 1 °C . In therapeutic ultrasound, the desired effect is often to heat the tissues. In the latter case temperatures up to 44 °C may be generated in the tissues.

Ultrasound waves are pressure waves. The pressure at any point is related to the intensity at that point. Pulsed ultrasound machines produce very large positive or negative pressures for very short periods of time. As Figure 13.2(a) showed, there will be a maxiumum and minimum intensity. Associated with these intensities are maximum (peak positive) and minimum (peak negative) pressures. As we have seen, the intensity I of the wave is related to the pressure amplitude by the equation

$$I = \frac{p^2}{2dc}$$

where d is the density of the medium and c is the speed of sound.

The high positive and negative pressures obtained using pulses of ultrasound can cause bubbles of gas to form which vibrate and collapse. These effects are known as cavitation and can cause large mechanical effects on the cells. One effect of cavitation may be to cause the cell membranes to burst. This usually results in cell death rather than cell mutation. Only a small number of cells are affected and so the damage is negligible in the adult. However, in the early stages of pregnancy cell death could be more serious. It is therefore considered inadvisable to use high-intensity pulsed fields on the foetus in the first three months of pregnancy. Cavitation may also produce free radicals which could have some of the same effects on the cells as ionising radiation.

Ultrasound used at the power levels normally encountered in diagnostic techniques (less than 100 mW cm^{-2}) has not yet been shown to produce any undesirable side-effects. For this reason it is a popular imaging technique, especially in sensitive areas such as obstetrics. However, there is some concern at the high peak power levels used in pulsed Doppler techniques. Here, peak power levels can be between 300 and 5000 mW cm^{-2}, with average power levels between 20 and 250 mW cm^{-2}. It is thought advisable not to use the latter devices on or near the foetus.

Summary

1. Ultrasound is sound in the range 20 Hz to 20 MHz.

2. Ultrasound is a pressure wave.

3. Ultrasound is produced by distorting a piezoelectric crystal by applying a rapidly varying voltage to opposite surfaces of the crystal.

4. Ultrasound is reflected from tissue boundaries. The fraction of the initial intensity of an ultrasound beam which is reflected depends on the density of the tissues and the speed of sound in them.

5. The intensity of an ultrasound beam is attenuated by the same fraction for each unit of distance the beam travels.

6. Units of intensity of ultrasound are given in decibels. The range of intensities produced by a probe is known as the dynamic range of the machine.

7. Ultrasound images are built up using the pulse –echo technique rather than using continuous waves.

8. There are four main kinds of ultrasound imaging machines, A, B, M and Doppler, and combinations and variations of these (Duplex, pulsed Doppler, etc.)

9. Ultrasound is used to measure the size of the foetus's head and body during pregnancy. It is used to examine the functioning of the heart and blood vessels in adults. It is used to look for tumours in the liver or breast or other organs.

10. Ultrasound is considered a very safe technique. No known damage has ever been done by using diagnostic ultrasound machines. However, care should be taken that pulsed Doppler ultrasound probes are not used near the foetus.

Questions

1. What range of frequencies do ultrasound waves have? Describe how an ultrasound wave is produced in a probe for an ultrasound scanner. What frequency would you choose for a probe used for imaging (a) the thyroid (b) the liver (c) the breast? Give reasons for your choices.

2. Explain the decibel scale. Why is it used in ultrasound scanning? If the intensity of a reflected wave I_r is 10^{-4} times the intensity of an original wave I_o, express the intensity of the reflected wave in terms of the original intensity in decibels.

3. Explain what you understand by the expression 'pulse –echo technique'. How is this used to produce an A-scan? What effect does attenuation have on an A-scan trace?

14 OTHER DIAGNOSTIC IMAGING TECHNIQUES

Magnetic resonance imaging

Magnetic resonance imaging or **MRI** is the latest, the most technologically complex and certainly the most expensive diagnostic imaging technique.

The phenomenon of nuclear magnetic resonance has been used extensively in the chemical analysis of small samples since its discovery in the 1940s. The rise in the use of X-ray computed tomography (Chapter 11) and the concurrent development of magnet technology and superconducting devices in the 1970s saw the development of the technique in medical imaging studies.

The basic principles of MRI require the use of a relatively large magnet, both in physical size and field strength. The magnet must be large enough to produce a highly uniform magnetic field (varying by <1 in 10^4) at field strengths of 0.1–2 tesla over sections of the body.

To produce this large magnetic field, different system designs have used **permanent**, **resistive** (electro-) or **superconducting** magnets. The different types of magnet have their own advantages and disadvantages.

A permanent magnet of 0.3 tesla may weigh more than 100 tonnes, but has little running costs after its initial, albeit high, purchase price. Similar strength resistive magnets weigh much less but consume upwards of 30 kW of electricity and require in-built cooling systems. Superconducting magnets, used particularly for field strengths above 0.2 tesla, have minimal power requirements but must be constantly maintained at temperatures of around 4 K (–269 °C) using liquid helium and liquid nitrogen (–196 °C) coolants to preserve the superconducting state. These coolants act as a 'heat buffer, to protect the liquid helium from the surrounding temperature.

Superimposed on this large magnetic field there are usually additional smaller magnetic fields with known gradients in two directions. These gradient fields produce a unique value of the magnetic field strength at each point within the instrument, Figure 14.1.

The purpose of the large magnetic field is to align all nuclei of certain types in the part of the body within the magnet to the direction of the field. These nuclei, which have odd numbers of protons and neutrons and which possess a property known as 'spin', effectively behave as tiny magnets. They will therefore align themselves with the applied magnetic field providing it is sufficiently strong.

Having achieved this alignment, the area under investigation is then subjected to pulses of radio frequency (RF) radiation. Given the correct frequency and direction, the RF pulses will supply energy to the nuclei and make them tip away from

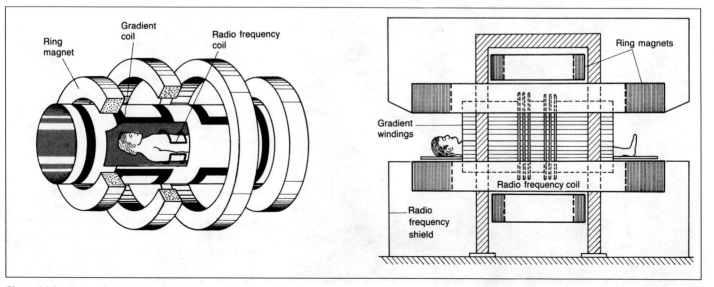

Figure 14.1   Magnetic resonance imager

the axis of alignment by either 90° or 180°, depending on the pulse.

Following the RF pulse, these 'magnetic' nuclei **precess**, or 'wobble', about the axis of the main field as the nuclei regain their alignment with that field.

The speed at which the nuclei return to that steady state gives rise to two parameters, known as the **T1 and T2 relaxation times**, which can be used to identify the nuclei.

The small changes in the magnetic field produced as the nuclei precess induce currents in a receiving coil which are digitised and then stored in a computer memory.

In practice a complex set of RF pulse sizes and sequences are used to obtain a variety of resonance signals. The use of these sequences and the unique value of the magnetic field strength within the investigated volume enable the resonance signals to be 'decoded' to give good estimations of the composition of the patient's tissues. This information can be reconstructed, as in X-ray computed tomography, to give images of that composition in three dimensions.

The technique of MRI is currently under a great deal of development, both clinically and technologically. The best clinical images are being obtained in neurological studies of the brain and central nervous system, but future progress is rapidly moving towards equally high quality images to be obtained throughout the rest of the body. Systems using the higher magnetic field strengths of 2 tesla and above may also allow detailed compositional studies to be done of complex molecules and their locations.

The principal advantage of MRI as a diagnostic imaging technique is related to the excellent image quality, which, given a highly uniform main magnetic field, can be of high resolution. Its other advantage is based on its apparent lack of harmful effects, unlike other diagnostic imaging techniques using ionising radiations which all carry some measure of risk.

The disadvantages of the technique are almost entirely related to its costs (upwards of £1 million), which have limited its widespread use within the NHS. These issues will be discussed at the end of the chapter.

Magnetic resonance imaging – Case study

A 26-year-old woman had been seen in the out-patient department following a referral from her general practitioner. She had been suffering bad persistent localised headaches for some time. Patients with symptoms such as these tend to worry that there may be some 'pathologic' reason for the headaches (such as cancer), causing considerable anxiety. Such causes must naturally be excluded.

A standard skull X-ray examination was done, and showed no abnormality. Following this, an X-ray computed tomography (CT) examination had also been carred out, since this would give more detailed, three-dimensional information. This also showed no abnormality.

The patient was then referred on to the MRI unit for further investigation, as this would provide the most detailed images available.

A series of sagittal 'slices' (parallel to the axis running from the front to the back of the patient) were then taken on the machine, weighted towards the parameter T1. The central 'slice' from this study is shown in Figure 14.2.

A great amount of detail can be seen, showing the bones of the skull, the covering layers of the brain and brain tissue, spinal cord and the upper vertebrae. This study was also completely normal, thus ruling out any likelihood that a direct so-called 'pathologic' cause was responsible for the headaches. The patient went on to have further biochemical investigations to see if these could reveal any possible cause.

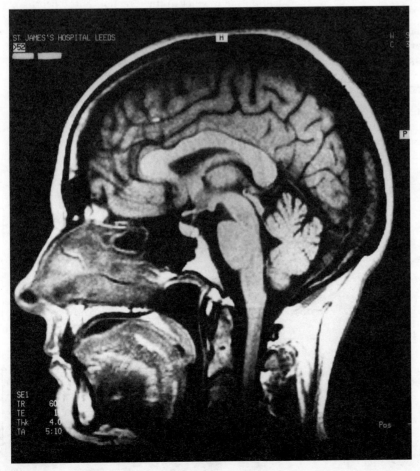

Figure 14.2   MRI midline (central) 'slice' through the head

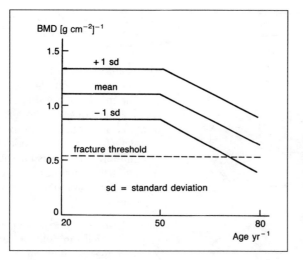

Figure 14.3 Change in mean and standard deviation of bone mineral density (BMD) in the lumbar spinal vertebra with age for normal UK women

It may seem somewhat surprising that MRI, being apparently free of hazard and providing the best anatomical detail, was done *after* the X-ray based skull and CT examinations. The reasons for this are twofold. At the time of writing the number of MRI machines in the UK used for routine patient studies is only in single figures. Additionally, as MRI is the most expensive equipment to purchase, operate and interpret, it tends to be reserved for those cases which have eluded diagnosis by other, relatively simpler or less expensive techniques.

Bone mineral determination

Osteopoenia and osteoporosis

Bones are made from a collagen matrix onto which bone mineral is laid down. The mineral is a calcium compound, and it gives strength to the bones in the same way that steel inserted into concrete gives it added strength. The bone matrix is continually being broken down and rebuilt during a person's lifetime and the mineral is reabsorbed into the blood and relaid onto the new matrix.

Bone mineral determination is necessary in the study of osteopoenia and osteoporosis.

Osteopoenia is the loss of bone mineral within the matrix. It is often a temporary, and reversible condition. One form of osteopoenia is the disease known as **rickets** in young children. Fortunately this is now rare in the UK. This disease occurs as a result of a lack of vitamin D. Vitamin D is necessary for the absorption of calcium with which to build the bone structure.

Osteoporosis is the loss of bone due to the loss of the matrix on which the bone minerals are laid down, and is an irreversible process. It can occur as a result of certain disease states such as kidney failure, bowel disease, or the use of steroids in extreme cases of asthma. In addition, the natural ageing process, particularly in women after the menopause (which usually occurs at about 50), can

lead to bone loss and subsequent osteoporosis. It is this latter process which is by far the most common cause of osteoporosis in Western societies today.

Three facts are important in the consideration of postmenopausal osteoporosis. The first is that the strength of the bones is proportional to the bone mineral contained in them. The second is that all women lose bone at the rate of 1% per annum after the menopause. The third is that in the UK, as well as in most countries of the Western world, we have an ageing population (there is an ever-increasing percentage of the population over the age of 75).

These three facts mean that there is now an increasing number of women who, because of a low bone mass at maturity, are living long enough for their bone loss to take them below a critical bone mass, as shown in Figure 14.3.

As a result, the key weight-bearing bones of the hip and spine become too weak, and fracture with the slightest accident. These fractures cause severe pain, and in some cases, premature death in elderly women. It should be realised that, as well as this suffering, the cost to the NHS in terms of operations and hospital stays alone is considered to be in terms of many millions of pounds per year.

It is now possible to measure a woman's bone mineral mass at maturity (between 45 and 55 usually), using a technique known as **bone densitometry**, and from that measurement predict which women will be at high risk of fracture by the time they are aged 80. The bone loss can then be halted by treatment with hormone replacement therapy, or slowed down with the aid of calcium, vitamin D and other drugs. There is thus a way to drastically reduce the suffering for large numbers of women (and consequent NHS costs).

Men are less likely to suffer from osteoporosis due to ageing. This is because they have more bone at maturity than women, and although they do lose bone with age, the onset of this loss occurs after the age of about 60. In addition, men have on average not lived as long as women.

Bone densitometry

The human trunk, in the vicinity of the lumbar vertebra and the top of the femur, where most osteoporotic fractures occur, can be approximated to a two-component system. These two components are lean soft tissue and bone.

Modern bone densitometers use an X-ray generator, producing pencil beams of X-rays, alternately of energies 85 kVp and 135 kVp. The intensities of these beams before passing through the trunk may be denoted by I_0 and I'_0, Figure 14.4. At any given position in the scan, the average thickness of the soft tissue (s) and bone (b) components within the beam are denoted by t_s and t_b respectively. The

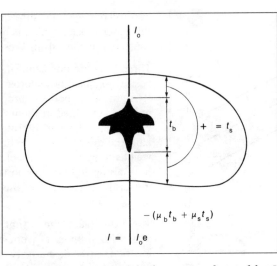

Figure 14.4 The attenuation of two beams *I* and *I'* of X-rays of different energies by bone, b, and soft tissue, s

attenuated intensities of the beams are denoted by *I* and *I'* respectively.

The linear attenuation coefficients for lean soft tissue are denoted by μ_s and μ'_s for the photon energies of the low-energy and high-energy beams respectively. Similarly the attenuation coefficients for bony tissue are denoted by μ_b and μ'_b respectively. Since the attenuation of the two photon beams by the two components is exponential, the following relationships hold:

$$I = I_0 \exp -(\mu_s t_s + \mu_b t_b)$$
$$I' = I'_0 \exp -(\mu'_s t_s + \mu'_b t_b)$$

Manipulating these equations leads to the expression:

$$t_b \propto \frac{\mu_s \ln(I') - \mu'_s \ln(I)}{\mu_s \mu'_b - \mu_b \mu'_s}$$

The use of two X-ray energies thus allows the soft tissue thickness to be eliminated from the equations. If only one energy was used, the total patient thickness at each scan position would need to be measured accurately – an impossible task. Alternatively the patient would need to be surrounded by a constant thickness of some tissue

mimicking material. Some early American workers in the field surrounded their patients with 'Play-Dough'!

The beam is moved backwards and forwards in steps across the body between the lumbar vertebrae and the middle of the thigh. At each position, the X-ray generator produces a pulse of X-rays at each of the two energies. From measurements of initial and detected X-ray intensities, together with the attenuation coefficients for soft tissue and bone at the two beam energies, the average thickness of bone in the beam at each point can thus be calculated.

The calculated value of bone thicknesses can then be represented much like a radionuclide or digital X-ray image, by the brightness of a pixel in a corresponding position on a television monitor. Such a scan is shown in Figure 14.5.

The areas of interest in a scan are usually the central three lumbar vertebrae and the femoral neck, as these are the main osteoporotic fracture sites causing pain and immobility. These areas of interest are located by an operator from the scan image, and the bone mineral mass for these areas is then automatically calculated by computer programs within the densitometer.

The values so obtained are compared with the normal range of values of bone mineral mass for women at the appropriate age. If the value lies below a calculated threshold value, then it is known that the patient being studied has a high risk of suffering osteoporosis in later life and steps can be taken to avert this.

As was mentioned earlier, currently the most favoured treatment for postmenopausal osteoporosis is a course of hormone replacement therapy (HRT) for a period of up to ten years. It is hoped that in a few years this treatment may be replaced with drugs known as diphosphonates, in order to avoid the side-effects that occur with HRT.

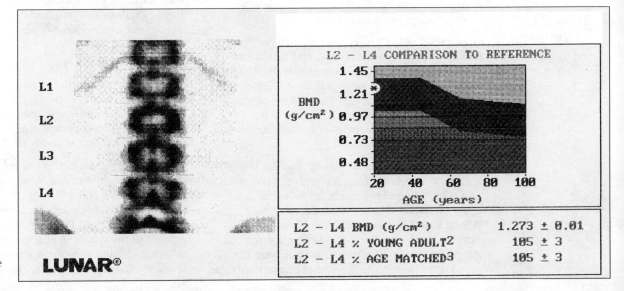

Figure 14.5 Bone densitometer scan

Diagnostic imaging – costs and effects

Modern diagnostic imaging techniques have increasingly become a vital part of the clinicians' armoury in Western medicine. However, the costs of such technology are high. At the time of writing (1991), the approximate prices of the various machines were:

Ultrasound scanner	£30 000
Osteoporosis scanner	£60 000
Gamma camera	£200 000
X-ray fluoroscopy system	£200 000
X-ray CT scanner	£500 000
Magnetic resonance imaging system	£1 000 000

Of course, the costs of such equipment are not restricted to their actual purchase price. The annual running costs of such high-technology equipment, which include the maintenance of the equipment and its so-called **consumables** (film, computer disks, etc.) frequently amount to ~10% of the initial capital cost. This figure does not include the salaries of the skilled staff who operate the machines and have to develop new techniques necessary to maximise the usefulness of the machines.

Further costs also arise since the machines must be replaced every 10 years or so, due to a combination of wear and a gradual obsolescence as new technology outperforms them. This effectively means that a further 10% of the purchase price per year has to be budgeted for.

A quick calculation will demonstrate that the total cost of providing a comprehensive diagnostic imaging service can quickly mount to massive proportions. However, what must then be remembered is that while the money is being spent on diagnostic imaging equipment, it cannot be spent on other things. For example:

Baby incubator	£4500
Foetal heart monitor	£6500
Hip replacement operation	£3000

Many drug treatments are also not without significant cost:

AIDS (9-day treatment course)	£1500
Ovarian cancer (course of chemotherapy)	£2000
Lung transplant (drugs to treat rejection, etc.)	£3500

Clearly, many other examples could be given. A quick glance through the figures will nevertheless demonstrate that the running of a modern hospital is a complex operation. It is easily possible to raise a number of questions regarding how the decisions are made on which treatment, operations or equipment should be bought. Just a small selection is given below:

(a) Do we perform 20 hip replacement operations now, or buy an osteoporosis scanner which might identify those women at risk and so allow the prevention of many more broken hips in 20 years' time?

(b) If we buy the ultrasound scanner this year, how will we afford another 20 courses of treatment for the expected AIDS patients?

(c) What will happen to the hospital's waiting list if we buy a new MRI machine?

The above examples are rather simplistic, since they exclude many other factors – the costs of doctors, nurses, porters, electricity, food, etc. Nevertheless, they serve to give an indication that modern medicine is a difficult business. Diagnostic imaging has a necessary and important role to play within this system, but must be considered in the widest possible context.

Bibliography

Aitken, M., *Osteoporosis in Clinical Practice*, Wright, 1984

Andersen, H.R. & Bergsten, O., *Blood Pressure Measurements and Methods*, S & W Medico Tecnik A/S Herdstedvang 8, Denmark

Ballantyne, J. & Martin, J.A.M. *Deafness*, Churchill Livingstone, 1984

Brown, B.H. & Smallwood, R.H., *Medical Physics and Physiological Measurement*, Blackwell Scientific Publications, 1981

De Grandis, L. (tr. Gilbert, J.), *Theory and Use of Colour*, Blandford Press

Greening, J.R., *Fundamentals of Radiation Dosimetry*, 2n edn, Adam Hilger, 1985

Guyton, A.C., *Textbook of Medical Physiology*, W.B. Saunders, 1986

Hill, D.W., *Physics Applied to Anaesthesia*, Butterworths, 1980

Holland, D., *Gastrointestinal Endoscopy; An Introduction for Assistants*, Balliere-Tindall, 1979

Horton, P.W., *Radionuclide Techniques in Clinical Investigations*, Adam Hilger, 1982

Hutchinson & Smith, 'NMR Clinical Results: Aberdeen', in Portain, James, Rollo, Rollo & Price, (eds), *Nuclear Magnetic Resonance (NMR) Imaging*, W.B. Saunders, 1983

Kathren, R.L., *Radiation Protection*, Adam Hilger, 1985

Kean, D.M. & Smith, M.L., *Magnetic Resonance Imaging: Principles and Applications*, Heinemann, 1986

Mackean, D. & Jones, B., *Introduction to Human and Social Biology*, 2nd edn, John Murray

Maran, A.G.D. (ed), 'The New Medicine: An Integrated System of Study, Volume 4', *Otorhinology including Oral Medicine and Surgery*, MTP Press Ltd, 1983

Mylroi, M.G. & Calvert, G., *Measurements and Instrumentation for Control*, IEE Control Engineering Series 26, Peter Peregrinus, 1984

NRPB, 'A Summary of Patient Doses in the UK', Report R-200, National Radiological Protection Board, 1986

Pavlidis, T., *Algorithms for Graphics and Image Processing*, Computer Science Press, 1982

Robinson, T.S., Price, R.R., Budinger, T.F., Fairbanks, V.F. & Pollycove, M., 'Radiation Absorbed Doses from Iron-52, Iron-55 and Iron-59 Used to Study Ferrokinetics', *Journal of Nuclear Medicine* **24**, 1983, 339–48

Scott, E.F., *Beginners' Guide to Microprocessors and Computing*, Bernard Bambini, 1980

Sheingold, D. (ed) *Transducer Interfacing Handbook: A Guide to Analog Signal Conditioning*, Analog Devices Inc., 1980

Shirley, I.M., Blackwell, R.J., Cusick, G., Farman, D.J. & Vicary, F.R., *A User's Guide to Diagnostic Ultrasound*, Pitman Medical, 1978

Stephenson, R.W., *Anatomy, Physiology and Optics of the Eye*, Henry Kimpton, 1973

Sumner, D., *Radiation Risks: An Evaluation*, Tarragon Press, 1987

Vaughan, D., Asbury, T. & Schaubert, L.V., *General Ophthalmology*, Lange Medical Publishing, 1980

Wall, B.F., Harrison, R.M. & Spiers, F.W., 'Patient Dosimetry Techniques', *Institute of Physical Sciences in Medicine Report 53*, 1988

Ward, C.S, *Electrical Safety in Hospitals*, Henry Kimpton, 1981

Waye, J.D., Geenen, J.E., Fleischer, D. & Venu, R.P., *Techniques in Therapeutic Endoscopy*, Gower Medical Publishing, 1987

Webb, S. (ed), *The Physics of Medical Imaging*, Adam Hilger, 1988

Wilkes, R.J., *Principles of Radiological Physics*, 2nd edn, Churchill Livingstone, 1987

Yost, W.A. & Nielson, D.W., *Fundamentals of Hearing*, Holt Rhinehart and Winston, 1977

Index